GALILEO
PUBLISHING

GIZA-GENESIS
THE BEST KEPT
SECRETS
Vol. I

Did the Author(s) of the
Book of Genesis and Exodus
Have Intimate Knowledge of the
Giza Pyramid Complex . . . or
Did They Blueprint it Themselves?

Howard Middleton-Jones
and
James M. Wilkie

A Galileo Publication
Tempe, Arizona
www.galileopublishing.com

A Galileo Publishing Publication
Tempe, Arizona, USA

Copyright, 2001 by Howard Middleton-Jones and James M. Wilkie

Middleton-Jones, Howard and Wilkie, James M.
Giza-Genesis: The Best-Kept Secrets, Volume 1, 2nd edition

Library of Congress Card Number 2002113581
ISBN 0971809836

Front cover artwork is a reconstruction based on the original cloth map, *Passage System of the Great Pyramid of Gizeh in the land of Egypt*, (June-July, 1909) which was included in a rare run of the book, *The Great Pyramid and Passages*, by Edgar Morton.

Cover & Interior Layout by Gary Fisher; crop circle photos, Lucy Pringle

A Galileo Publication
www.galileopublishing.com

"Deep beneath the Plateau, situated among the many subterranean passageways throughout the Thura limestone, is a particular chamber. Located within this chamber is what we will call "The Crystal." This crystal is best described as a machine which, when aligned, forms the constellation of stars as they appeared aeons ago." (Chapter 8)

"Comet Lee was highly instrumental in triggering events towards the Sun's birth of our newest planet.. That planet is presently forming inside our very Solar System. On December 21, 2000, it will be expelled from the Sun, and find itself in an orbit slightly offset of the orbit of the inner planets that are presently orbiting the Sun within our Solar System.

"This new planet will continue on its ejected orbital path, while simultaneously continuing to solidify, until — yes, you guessed it! — December 21, 2012. At that time it will shift into the same orbital path along with the other existing inner planets. In the book of Genesis, in the story of Cain and Abel, this event is described as the "birth of Cain." (Chapter 8)

"Those anomalous objects (termed Sun Cruisers — and there are now at least two) are in fact Plasma Carriers, of gigantic proportions, said to be in excess of three thousand miles across! The carriers will initiate an artificial disturbance within the sun, causing the sun to eject two massive Coronal Mass Ejections (CME's). The trajectory of these CME's will be directed at earth, at which time all satellites will be placed out of commission, as will the entire power grid. It is at this point that we, too, will enter into the war with the Draconians. BELIEVE IT!" (Chapter 9)

"On May 3, 2000, a certain three individuals independently (physically and actually) made their way to Cairo for a rendezvous. These three individuals, up to this point, had no idea as to what event was about to unfold. They only knew that their previous training and unique skills would be required. It was here that they were given the co-ordinate entry points . . .

"... On the night of May 3, the individuals, physically and actually, utilized both entry points, since at that point in time it was not possible to send all three down the Bethlehem Processionway. It was here that two very old "Booby trap" explosive devices were subsequently disarmed.

"... Most of what occurred during the late hours of May 4 when this team made entry, using the Bethlehem Processionway was described on the Jeff Rense Sightings show archived audiotape of the interview of May 8, 2000. However, what you did not hear described in the interview, is an event that occurred, of which we knew nothing, prior to having advanced the "Crystal." We were unable to share this event with anyone, as per "His" request. (Chapter 14)

Acknowledgements

The front cover is a reconstruction based on the original cloth map, Passage System of the Great Pyramid of Gizeh in the land of Egypt, (June-July 1909) which was included in a rare run of the book The Great Pyramid and Passages, by Edgar Morton.

Contents of this book are the result of many years of original research, reflected in the graphically displayed constructed models and illustrations. For these we are indebted to the assistance of Jeff Didham of Winnipeg (Envisage Design Group) Canada.

We would also like to thank Jan Merta, Ph.D., co-founder of Ambilac, and John Thorvaldson and Gail Young for their support and encouragement in the on-going research at Ambilac. In addition, we are grateful to Julie King, one of our more recent associate researchers from Australia, who has contributed a great deal toward the understanding of more recent events. The relevant section of her work is included in the Appendix.

The following people have continuously contributed towards our research, and to them we also offer our appreciation; Edmund Meadows of Viking Remote Viewing, David and Virginia Kingston, University of Life, Brian Stokes of Swansea Astronomical Society for assistance in constructing and checking the relevant star charts, and Kent Steadman of Cyberspace Orbit.

The Crop circle photographs were taken by Lucy Pringle, one of the most dedicated researchers, photographers and authors in this exciting field.

May we also take this opportunity to thank Irin Smith, our publisher, for her contributions to perservering and bringing forth this work under unusual cirucumstances and events.

Note by Publisher: After many requests from the public, this is the third edition and printing of Volume 1 of the Giza Genesis Disclosure Series. The number and quality of original images were a challenge for layout and we thank Gary Fisher for going above and beyond preparing the layout.

Author's Note

We offer this publication as a timely store of new knowledge and understanding derived from our research concerning the connection between the Giza Plateau, Egypt, and the Old Testament books of Genesis and Exodus. It is hoped that this understanding will assist those on Planet Earth in coming to terms to what is about to occur in this part of the Solar System.

"Knowledge is Power," as the saying goes, and we believe that this aphorism is critical throughout the book.

The information contained in this publication is the result of many years of meticulous research, encompassing a broad spectrum of subject matter. The results are based on the best available information and sources, utilizing the best applications available at our disposal. In the majority of cases, the sheer amount of data presented would have required several texts alone. However, in order to bring to the reader the most complete understanding as possible, we have attempted to summarize this plethora of data into one single text.

We would also like to quote another proverb: "One seeing is worth a thousand tellings." Thus, illustrations form an integral part of this work and we have included them wherever possible in order to offer a full awareness and understanding of the analysis. Combined with the depth of textual content, we trust that the reader will come to a realization concerning the experiences that we here on Earth are about to undergo.

The sections from the Holy Bible were extracted from the New American Bible, the Catholic Press, Chicago 1970.

Authors' Addenda

Because of the growing interest in our research and the need to convey what is occurring in our solar system and beyond, combined with the fact we experienced a severe book distribution problem last year, we have come back with a vengeance and a new publisher.

This, and subsequent volumes of the Giza Genesis trilogy series will be published over a short time frame, thus providing an informative understanding of the background of the present planetary changes we are witnessing today.

In this, volume 1, we decipher and explain the complete layout of the Giza Plateau and how it relates to the Book of Genesis. In doing this we have attempted to construct a bridge between the banks of "science and religion" thus making a connection over the murky dark waters of our ancient origins.

In Volume 2 we will delve even deeper into this understanding and offer additional evidence as to who actually constructed the Giza Plateau site and for what purpose. While in the final Volume of the trilogy we attempt to piece together the diverse fragments of this cosmic jigsaw in order to complete the overall intended picture. To demonstrate this understanding we explain the purpose of the construction of the Plateau, what does it mean to us today and why we need to understand the "great plan" in order to prepare for the coming earth changes.

Contents

Illustration List

Preface

Introduction

Chapter 1: The Cosmic Jig-Saw Puzzle 1

Chapter 2: The Giza-Genesis Connection 9

Chapter 3: 2012 – Khufu And The Ark 39

Chapter 4: The Covenant – Or The Crystal 57

Chapter 5: The Book Of Exodus 63

Chapter 6: The Great Step 88

Chapter 7: Edgar's Revenge 101

Chapter 8: Crystal Clear 110

Chapter 9: The Final Countdown 119

Chapter 10: The Erideans 127

Chapter 11: The Great Experience – The Plan And The Purpose........133

Chapter 12: Interdimensional Physics 141

Chapter 13: Drawings – The Analysis 155

Chapter 14: The 8th Day – The Crystal And Global Grid Activation 169

Chapter 15: Synopsis of Volume 1 With An Introduction to Volume 2 188

Appendices 197

Appendix A: Parallel Universes, by Wayne Moody

Appendix B: The Universal Grid

Appendix C: Summary of the Theses and Research

Appendix D: Time Line

Bibliography 217

Authors 218

Index 219

List of Illustrations

Chapter One
Figure 1.1 - Osiris
Figure 1.2 - Thoth
Figure 1.3 - Isis

Chapter Two
Figure 2.1 - Aerial Model of Plateau
Figure 2.2 - Three-Star Crop Circle, Wiltshire
Figure 2.3 - Low Resolution Screenshot from NASA VRML
Figure 2.4 - Pyramid of Menkaure
Figure 2.5 - Pyramids of Menkaure, Khafre and Khufu
Figure 2.6 - Pyramid of Khafre

Chapter Three
Figure 3.1 - Adam - Seth Lineage Chart
Figure 3.2 - Seth-Enosh Line
Figure 3.3 - Mahalel Line
Figure 3.4 - Enoch Line
Figure 3.5 - Methuselah Line
Figure 3.6 - Lamech Line
Figure 3.7 - Noah Line Chart
Figure 3.8 - Intersect to Queens' Chamber
Figure 3.9 - Meridian Point of Hidden Chamber
Figure 3.10 - Meridian Point of Hidden Chamber;
            Noah Line and Intersection of Grand Gallery
Figure 3.11 - Pyramid Plateau Layout
Figure 3.12 - Plateau Model No. 1
Figure 3.13 - Plateau Model No. 2
Figure 3.14 - Plateau Model No. 3
Figure 3.15 - Plateau Model No. 4
Figure 3.16 - Earth-Venus-Mercury Model Layout No.1
Figure 3.17 - Earth-Venus-Mercury Model Layout No. 2
Figure 3.18 - Earth-Venus-Mercury Model Layout No. 3
Figure 3.19 - Temple Valley Floor Plans
Figure 3.20 - Overlay of Temple floor Plans
Figure 3.21 - Bob Lazar's Flying Saucer and Annihilation Reactor Chamber
Figure 3.22 - Opening of Cheop's Pyramid No. 1
Figure 3.23 - Opening of Cheop's Pyramid No. 2

Illustration List continued...

Chapter Four
Figure 4.1 - Plateau Layout Model No. 5
Figure 4.2 - Plateau Layout Model No. 6
Figure 4.3 - Great Pyramid Diagram, Showing Layers
Figure 4.4 - Inner Layout of Great Pyramid by Morton

Chapter Five
Figure 5.1 - The Grand Gallery No. 1
Figure 5.2 - The Four Pins
Figure 5.3 - The Grand Gallery No. 2
Figure 5.4 - The Ledges and Tables
Figure 5.5 - The Grand Gallery No. 3
Figure 5.6 - Cups and Pitchers
Figure 5.7 - Showbread
Figure 5.8 - Grand Gallery No.4 Showing the Lampstands
Figure 5.9 - Grand Gallery - Side View
Figure 5.10 - The Cemented Ledges
Figure 5.11 - The Seven Girdle Stones
Figure 5.12 - The Various Sections and Parts
Figure 5.13 - The Five Sheets Sewn Together
Figure 5.14 - The 25 Holes on Each Side (with)
Figure 5.15 - Wings fitted into the 25 holes
Figure 5.16 - The Unit
Figure 5.17 - The Post and Mortice
Figure 5.19 - The Wings
Figure 5.20 - The Veil
Figure 5.21 - The Boards and Veil
Figure 5.22 - The Pattern Shown to Us
Figure 5.23 - The Table and Lampstand
Figure 5.24 - The Operating Mechanism
Figure 5.25 - The Girdle Stones
Figure 5.26 - The Step
Figure 5.27 - North End of Gallery
Figure 5.28 - The Great Gallery Mechanism

Illustration List continued...

Chapter Six

Figure 6.1 - The Step
Figure 6.2 - The Three Granite Plugs
Figure 6.3 - Red Granite and the Girdles
Figure 6.4 - Great Pyramid Internal Layout No. 1
Figure 6.5 - Great Pyramid Internal Layout No. 2
Figure 6.6 - The Great Pyramid Entrance
Figure 6.7 - Great Pyramid - Internal Layout No. 3
Figure 6.8 - Great Pyramid - Internal Layout No. 4
Figure 6.9 - Great Pyramid - Internal Layout No. 5

Chapter Seven

Figure 7.1 - Great Pyramid - General Internal Model
Figure 7.2 - Great Pyramid - Internal South Wall
Figure 7.3 - Great Pyramid - Internal North Wall
Figure 7.4 - Plateau Model Layout A
Figure 7.5 - Plateau Model Layout B
Figure 7.6 - Plateau Model Layout C
Figure 7.7 - Plateau Model Layout D

Chapter Nine

Figure 9.1 - Eclipse Crop Circle
Figure 9.2 - Solar Stargate

Chapter 10

Figure 10.1 - The Winged Disc

Chapter 12

Figure 12.1 - Autocad Model No. 1
Figure 12.2 - Autocad Model No 2
Figure 12.3 - Planet Mercury - Inner Core
Figure 12.4 - Crop Circle Rings and 12.5 - The Inner Planets
Figure 12.6 - The Inner Rings on the Planets and
Figure 12.7 - Crop Circle
Figure 12.8 - Sun Giving Birth to Our New Planet 12.8
Figure 12.9 - The 12 Houses

Figure 12.10 - Solar Grid No. 1
Figure 12.11 - Solar Grid No. 2
Figure 12.12 - Solar Grid No. 3
Figure 12.13 - Solar Grid No. 4
Figure 12.14 - Solar Grid No. 5
Figure 12.15 - Final Grid
Figure 12.16 - The 12 Houses A
Figure 12.17 - The 12 Houses B
Figure 12.18 - The 12 Houses C
Figure 12.19 - The Houses and Stars
Figure 12.20 - The 144 Stars
Figure 12.21 - Crop Circle
Figure 12.22 - Star Chart Alignment

Chapter 13

Figure 13.1 - Plateau Drawing - Decipher No. 1
Figure 13.2 - Plateau Drawing - Decipher No. 2
Figure 13.3 - Plateau Drawing - Decipher No. 3
Figure 13.4 - Plateau Drawing - Decipher No. 4
Figure 13.5 - Plateau Drawing - Decipher No. 5
Figure 13.6 - Solar Stargate
Figure 13.7 - Star Chart A
Figure 13.8 - Star Chart B

Chapter 14

Figure 14.1 - SOHO Solar Image
Figure 14.2 - SOHO Anomaly Enlargement
Figure 14.3 - Stargate
Figure 14.4 - Proton Flux Chart
Figure 14.5 - Radar Ring
Figure 14.6 - Solar Torpedo
Figure 14.7 - Solar Coronal Mass Ejection (CME)
Figure 14.8 - C3 Satellite Image of a CME
Figure 14.9 - Seismograph – USA
Figure 14.10 - Brookhaven Laboratories - Long Island - Radar Ring
Figure 14.11 - Solar Anomaly
Figure 14.12 - Plateau Model
Figure 14.13 - The "Solar Cruiser"
Figure 14.14 - Solar Satellite Image Showing the Pleiades

Illustration List continued...

Chapter 15
Figure 15.1 - Plateau - Top View
Figure 15.2 - Plateau - Hall of Records Main Frame No. 2
Figure 15.3 - Plateau - Main Frame No. 2
Figure 15.4 - Plateau - Main frame No.3
Figure 15.5 - Plateau - Main Frame No.4
Figure 15.6 - Plateau - Hall of Records and Tomb Locations
Figure 15.7 - Full Plateau Model 120 Degrees Rotation,
                    The Bethlehem Processionway
Figure 15.8 - Full Plateau Model - 0-120-240 Degrees
Figure 15.9 - May 5th Plateau Alignment - Star Chart
Figure 15.10 - May 5th Star Alignment
Figure 15.11 - Overview of Volume 2 A
Figure 15.12 - Overview of Volume 2 B
Figure 15.13 - Overview of Volume 2 C
Figure 15.14 - All 12 Houses - Top View
Figure 15.15 - Volume 2 D
Figure 15.16 - Volume 2 E

Appendix
Figure App. 1 – The Universal Grid

Preface

One of the greatest challenges when compiling any article, book or paper is the dilemma of where, and in this case, when, to start. The answer is obvious to some: at the beginning! But how do you define "beginning," or even "end," if there is none?

The purpose of this book and others to follow in the Genesis-Giza Disclosure Series is to deliver to the general public information about vitally important global events that are now occurring. In order to understand the dynamics of these major events and their potential impact on our lives, it is important to have a basic understanding of our origins on the planet and in this part of the cosmos. This understanding requires information on a diverse number of subjects.

What we are about to present is certainly no easy task, and by no means are we attempting to offer the definitive "guide to the universe." We are well aware that some of the related concepts and conclusions may appear bizarre to some, but in the majority of cases, we have attempted to offer background explanation and evidence whenever available.

It is hoped that the contents of this book will assist and guide those of you with a burning desire to have answers to some of the major questions concerning the birth of humanity – whenever that was!

Questions such as: Are we alone? How did we evolve on this planet? Where were we before earth? Why are we presently experiencing an increasing number of earthquakes and anomalous weather patterns? And, for some people, even more profound questions, such as: Who actually built the Pyramids of the Giza Plateau, and why? And — Is there really a Hall of Records under the Giza Plateau?

Believe it or not, all of these issues are inextricably linked. The information we present here is one of the biggest mind-blowing revelations ever imparted in the history of humankind. In certain circles, this information has either been covered or withheld from the public domain; or it is so complex, it has been "lost" in the gigantic web of misunderstanding and misinterpretation.

As we proceed to unravel this web that includes natural and physical planetary and cosmic events, mythological stories, inspired books of wisdom and folklore, symbolic representations of human and cosmic connections, and actual physical remains of ancient civilizations, we hope you will share our amazement, and awe. We know you will begin to realize as we did, that we are engaged in reconstituting a gigantic cosmic jig saw. Piece by piece, all of these diverse aspects seem to fit together.

We will take you on a voyage of discovery that journeys back in time to witness the very beginnings of earth and its early inhabitants, to the development of the early great civilisations of Sumeria, Mesopotamia and Egypt, and others. This incredible journey will explain not only our true origins, but perhaps it will be one of self-discovery as well. It is hoped that the ultimate blueprint that unfolds on this journey will assist you and a multitude of others on the planet today towards an understanding and preparation for what undoubtedly will come to pass in the coming months and years.

Introduction

We on this planet we call earth (Terra) are rapidly approaching a cosmic watershed. This watershed will completely alter or strengthen, as the case may be, the concept of one's belief in the evolution and advancement of humankind. It will be a time when many profound questions will be answered. In this book, we offer the most compact understanding of the origins of humankind in our solar system, simultaneously untangling the complex weave of "myth," reality and linguistic interpretations of the book of Genesis. Over the swirling mists of time, the contents of Genesis have been subjected to countless translations and interpretations. While analyzing these contents, scholars discovered a strong connection to the layout of the Giza Plateau Pyramid complex in Cairo, Egypt.

Whoever wrote the texts of Genesis was in possession of the knowledge of the exact mathematical and astronomical layout of the Giza Plateau pyramid complex. Also, the obverse would be true. Utilizing not just the pyramids themselves, but the complete layout of the Giza Pyramid complex in conjunction with the texts of Genesis, we will demonstrate the true purpose of this magnificent and intriguing site. In the past, Egyptologists seemed to have followed only one path after Champollin[1] "deciphered" the Rosetta stone in the 1820's. One of the major drawbacks of any research that uses only one interpretation to follow the "treasure trail" they are seeking, is the limited meaning this places on subsequent findings.

Our task is to open new trails and paths in order to demonstrate the true meaning of what the ancient Egypt legacy is really all about. In this book we will provide new ammunition and a map for the increasing breeds of truth seekers. As we progress through our understanding that emanates from sources left in text and stone, we will discover even more profound and crucial revelations concerning our very existence and advancement in the cosmos. These are revelations that some among us may wish to cover up, in a feeble attempt to prevent our free will choice, or opportunity to "ascend" to a higher level of understanding and awareness. Initially, because we wanted this vital and timely information to reach as many in the public domain as possible, we placed a number of essential articles on the Internet. However, in order for the complete explanation to be offered as one package and to reach those who have limited access to the Internet or no access at all, this series of books now brings the full disclosure to everyone. Thus, we begin our journey.

---

1. Champollin, Jean-François (1790-1832) - Known by many as the "Father of Egyptology" because of his decipherment of the Rosetta stone in 1822.

Chapter 1

The Cosmic Jig-Saw Puzzle

The earth was a formless wasteland, and darkness covered the abyss, while a mighty wind swept over the waters.

— Genesis 1: 2

This traditional concept is what we are led to believe according to the Bible texts. But what about the much older "mythological," archaeological and geological evidence?

Until the mid-twentieth century, human fossil records were sparse and specimen dating was limited. However, modern dating techniques now help to determine the age of these fossils. In the last 50 years, the number of human fossil discoveries has increased greatly. Some of the largest of these were Leakey's find at Olduvai Gorge in 1960s in Kenya's Turkana Basin, and the discovery of the remains of "Lucy" in Ethiopia by Johanson's group.

All of these discoveries in their own way have advanced the knowledge of human origins. **They have also shown us that human evolution of the hominid family has been one of repeated evolutionary trial and error.**

Thus, are we to assume that "Homo sapiens" is the lone hominid?

THE GIZA-GENESIS CONNECTION

Utilizing the texts of Genesis in combination with the complete layout of the Giza Plateau Pyramid complex, we offer one of the most far-reaching and profound discoveries thus far divulged to the public. *By interpreting the meaning and purpose of the complete layout of the Pyramid complex, we can decipher our real origins and purpose on this planet, including the events occurring today!*

THE ANCIENT EGYPTIAN CONCEPT

The question of ancient mythologies, whether Egyptian, Mayan, Asian, etc., and the correlation of additional ancient texts often raises the "fact or fiction," "myth or reality" scenario. What if the whole concept of these "myths" were but one and the same, albeit confused and misinterpreted over the swirling mists of time?

This is precisely what we intend to illustrate. However, we venture further than any others, "boldly going where no others have gone before." In this book, we will cover many issues and areas of exploration where perhaps even many an angel would fear to tread. *Were we in fact originally evolved from the primordial slime of the very beginnings of embryonic earth? Or were we "genetically modified" – "terra-formed" — by a distant advanced civilization?* An increasing number of people are now beginning to question traditional and fundamental beliefs of our origins on this "third rock from the sun," especially in light of the increasing number of anomalous archaeological finds.

THE HISTORY OF PLANET EARTH

Planet Earth, as we know it today is said to have been in existence for over 50,000 million years. In the geological period of earth, traditionally known as the "Cambrian" – approximately 510 million years ago – we are informed that continental events covered a diverse time frame. Such events included the break-up of the ancient south polar super continent of Rodina with its subsequent re-assembly of Godwara and Laurussia, the super continent of Pangaea, or "all land." Resulting fragmentation of these gigantic tracts of land led to the continental pattern with which we are familiar today.

Throughout its history, Earth experienced many ages of now classified geological periods, from the Cambrian and Ordovician, circa 470 million years ago, through the Silurian and Devonian, 400 million years ago, to the Jurassic and finally the Cenozoic, 40 million years ago. In this final period, Africa moved northward, consolidating much of the southern European land fragments, thus creating the Pyrenees; and the Himalayan mountain range rose upward. This period has often been called The Age of Mammals.

One of the largest and most complete collections of human fossil remains (unearthed at Zhoukoudian, near Beijing) vanished in 1941 after being entrusted to a platoon of US Marines. The cave site of Sima de los Huesos in Spain, under excavation since 1988, has yielded more than 80% of all known Middle Pleistocene post-cranial fossil human remains. These finds produced a jigsaw of many species, of which a larger number are extinct.

In addition, Vince Sarich and Allan Wilson, of the University of California, Berkeley, carried out an analysis of molecular evidence for relationships among apes and age of divergence between apes and humans. The degree of protein similarity in different species (kinship) establishes a "molecular clock" for past evolution. Application of this analysis of blood protein led them to conclude that divergence between chimps and humans could not have happened prior to five million years ago. The DNA has confirmed these results.

Chimps and gorillas are more closely related to humans than orang-utans, since chimps share more than 99% of genetic material with humans, even though the chromosomes are packaged in a different way.

Wilson, Cann and Stoneking (Berkeley 1987) produced a tree diagram showing affinities of mitochondrial DNA, material only transmitted through the maternal line. The diagram showed that the people of African origins display greatest variation in their mitochondria; and although other modern populations were rooted within the African variation, their common ancestors were only 200,000 years old (The "African Eve" hypothesis).

Thus, the African populations demonstrate the largest genetic variation, whereas the common ancestor of all modern people is thought to have originated some 200,000 to 100,000 years ago.

This is all very interesting and contributes to our understanding of the makeup of our more recent ancestors. However, it does not really explain the reason for such diversity on this little planet. So many mysteries and so many unanswered questions on such a small, now third rock, from the sun!

Same Characters, Different Names?

The world consists of a multitude of races and religions, all with their own beliefs, myths and agendas. However, if we look at this array of concepts, we discover a constant theme throughout. The "Virgin" birth, the death and resurrection, are closely followed by a continuous tie-in of the heavens and heavenly bodies.

There arose out of the darkness a great shining egg,
and this was Re.

Again, according to the ancient Egyptian mythologies, before there was any land, all was in darkness, the void, and a great waste of water known as the Nun. From this arose Ra (Sun).

I am Khepera at the dawn and Ra at noon, and Tem in the evening.

The sun was the most important of the Egyptian deities and possessed many names. As a sun disk, he was called Aten. As the rising sun, he was known as Khepri, the great scarab beetle, rolling before him the globe of the sun just as this beetle rolls before it a ball of dung on earth — where it lays its eggs and from which bursts forth life. As the sun climbed the zenith he was known as Ra (or Re), the supreme god of Heliopolis, (the City of Light) and as he set, he was known as an old man, Atum. He was also named Horus (face), and when this aspect was combined with that of Ra, Ra-Harakhte was seen as the young sun of the horizon, a winged sun disk. He was born each morning as a golden calf from the heavenly cow and swallowed every night by the celestial woman, to be reborn again the next day.

The moon was the sun's brother and son of Nut (Nuit) the sky. Often he was identified with Osiris (Ausar)[1] god of the underworld and resurrection. Other times, he was identified with Thoth, architect and god of learning; and ultimately keeper of the "Key" and overseer of the "weighing of the heart and feather."

Thus we have Nun, or Nu, chaos or the primordial waste; Atum, the "completed one," also known as Neb-er-djer (Lord to the limit); and Ra personifying the sun in its strength and identified with the creator god Atum. Ra himself was said to have ruled on earth during the "Zep Tepi," The First Time, when men and gods lived together on this planet.

Born from these gods were: Shu, movement of light in the air, the "now'; and Tefnut, the twin sister of Shu, known as the "spitter." Tefnut is moisture in all forms; condensation, humidity, orgasm, ejaculation and all bodily processes producing wetness.

Also born from these gods was Geb, the oldest one, the round earth, the ground of reality upon which all living souls are met. Geb, the earth, and Nut, the sky, are the original lovers, but separated by Shu, the atmosphere; thus representing the movement of now or the present, separating the past (Geb) from the future (Nut). It is said that Geb is the latent power of inanimate matter, to waken consciousness out of itself by the light of the soul.

Nut is the goddess of the sky and often represented as a woman with an elongated body arched over the earth, supported by Shu and separated from Geb during the day. She descended to Geb each night, thus creating darkness. From Nut were conceived Osiris, Horus, Set, Isis and Nephthys.

Ra acknowledged Osiris as his heir, and is said to have fathered both

Osiris and Horus. Thoth is said to have fathered Isis, and Geb to have fathered only Set and Nephthys.

EGYPTIAN DEITIES

Nu

(The primordial, stagnant ocean)

The creation of **Atum** - The first event

Ra (or Re)

Ra, the sun-god. **Ra-Atum,** the coming of the light

and symbolized by the Phoenix

Birth of Twins

A son **Shu** – god of air and daughter **Tefnut** – goddess of world order

(The Twins were raised by **Nu** and supervised **by Ra-Atum's** eye.)

Shu and **Tefnut** gave birth to

Geb – god of earth

His wife and sister was **Nut,** goddess of the sky.

Geb and **Nut** were parents of

Isis, Osiris, Nephthys, and Set.

Isis **and** Osiris **gave birth to**

Horus

The above gods were considered to be the grouping known as the "Ennead".

Osiris and Isis fell in love while still in the womb, and therein produced Horus the elder (Heru-Ur). There have been many versions of the myth of Osiris, but basically it was Osiris that fell prey to the plot of the 72 conspirators (72 x 2 = 144 or 12 x 12) determined to do away with him. In the 28th year of his reign on the 17th day of the month of Hathor, (13th Baktun in the Mayan calendar) late September, which up to December is four months in total, Osiris fell to the conspirators and his body was cast into the Nile by Set. With the help of Thoth, Nephthys, Anubis and Horus, Isis restored Osiris to life. Osiris could have re-claimed the throne but preferred to maintain his kingdom in the land of the dead. It was left to Horus to avenge his father.

Followers of Set, or Seth, seem to have worshipped him under crocodile (reptilian) fetishes. Osiris was represented as a mummified king, his body colored red for the earth or green for vegetation. On his head he wore the *atef* crown, composed of the white crown of Upper Egypt, and the two red feathers ofBusiris. The cult of Osiris originated in Abydos, where his actual tomb was said to be located.

Figure 1.1 — Osiris   Figure 1.2 — Thoth

Figure 1.3 — Isis [Left]

Horus, Hor meaning face, was the falcon god; at first a sky god, with the sun and moon as its eyes. Later, the falcon came to symbolize a warrior god and victorious leader. As Horus the elder, he was patron deity of Upper Egypt. After the conquering of Set and unification of Egypt (circa 3100 BCE)[2] he became the patron deity of both Upper and Lower Egypt.

These nine gods of the Ennead are the foremost deities of the Egyptian pantheon. They were also called "The Great Ennead of Heliopolis," the original religious capital of Egypt and the sacred city of Ra.

Central to the Egyptian's understanding of the universe was that man was made in the image of god, Ra. From that man emerged the image of all creation.

RESURRECTION "MYTHS"

A plethora of tales surrounds the resurrection concept in a diverse number of countries and religions. Apart from the "Jesus resurrection," many of them, such as the eastern savior god Virishna (circa 1200 BCE) seem to originate from the Caucasus mountain region in modern northern Iraq (Mesopotamia). The following are just a few examples of a number of similar and equivalent "resurrection" myths. All of the individuals were "sons of god," born of a virgin mother, and they "died" in order that our sins could be forgiven. They were all "born" on December 25th — the period of the regeneration of the sun;symbols, for instance, were chosen carefully from the natural world, as a method to express a specific principle. A common motif is a queen sniffing a lotus flower. The perfume given off is its spiritualized essence; does this remind one of the odor of sanctity in the Christian doctrine? In the large necropolis of Saqqara, just south of Cairo, lie the remains of the tomb of Unas, reputedly 5th dynasty, whose pyramid has long since decayed. Ancient religious texts, said to be the oldest surviving, show the funerary journey of Osiris. They reveal that upon his death he was taken to a city called "On." and all were symbolically crucified at the spring equinox when the sun enters the sign of Aries the ram — when light triumphs over darkness. These resurrected beings include Khrishna of Hundostan, Buddha Sakia of India, Osiris and Horus of Egypt, Odin of Scandinavia, Zoroaster of Persia, Baal and Taut of Phoenicia, Indra of Tibet, Jao of Nepal, Tammuz of Syria and Babylon, the son of Odin, and Promethus of the Caucasus.

Whatever point of origin one takes, myth and symbolism are intertwined. Whereas myth is a chosen means for communicating knowledge, symbolism is a powerful way of representing a concept to evoke an understanding.

From there, the body of Osiris was taken across the Nile to a place called Khem, where the body remained for 70 days.

Eventually, Osiris was taken south to Rostau (Giza Plateau) and the center of the Duat, the portal or gateway between the upper and lower world. From here his body entered the fortress of Osiris and traveled downward through a gateway, where his soul (Ba) was said to have gone to the star Alnitak in the Orion constellation. Thus, he was known as the god of Orion.

The texts describe Isis as saying:

> *Tell me thy name, divine Father;*
> *for the man shall live who is called by his name.*
> *Then answered Ra:"I created the heavens and the earth,*
> *I ordered the mountains, I made the great and wide sea,*
> *I stretched out the two horizons like a curtain.*
> *I am he who openeth his eyes and it is light,*
> *and who shutteth them and it is dark.*
> *At his command the Nile riseth,*
> *but the gods know not his name.*
> *I am Khepera in the morning, I am Ra at noon, I am Tem at eve."*

The symbolism of Jesus and Osiris seem to be the same. Both were embodied in the celestial events of Orion; both were sons of "god" and sons of kings; both died and resurrected; both held the key to eternal life for their people. On the September 21, 1999 at dawn on the Giza plateau, Orion, the symbol of the resurrection, was in the same position when the solar eclipse took place at the crucifixion of Christ. Orion seems to be the Osiris-Jesus symbolism of eternal life, placing the map of the heavens in the correct positions for this century. (Moroney 1999)From the above, we can see how many characters in our "play" or set of "myths" may be misinterpreted or perhaps misunderstood. The situation may appear similar, but the names may change, depending upon the relevant civilization or cultural environment. This is an important factor to bear in mind when analyzing these ancient myths, in order to re-evaluate the real underlying intention, or purpose, of the original message. In other words, one must be able to stand back in order to take in the much larger picture that is presented to the viewer. Therefore, it is essential to understanding the key to the picture presented, not to take the names of our characters and the associated numbers too literally. One must remember that these names and numbers change in relation to the context and point of reference of the story being read.

To demonstrate this in the case of Osiris, we have read that Seth and his 72 conspirators cut him into 14 pieces that were scattered over Egypt. What was so significant about the number 72, that it should be recorded throughout history? Later in the book, we will look at this in detail. Thus, with this background knowledge, we now venture forward in our search for truth and understanding.

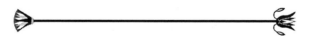

Notes

1. Ausar: There is only one god in the Nile Valley, but that god had many attributes and qualities, or *neters*, or gods. That is, they are divine entities but, merely part of the creator. The three most important *neters* were *Heru* (Horus), *Auset* (Isis) and *Ausar* (Osiris). Heru, son of Ausar and Auset, is represented by a falcon, which was chosen because of its ability to soar high in the sky and look down at man, like God. His right eye represents the sun, and like God, almost nothing on Earth escapes the sun. Heru also represents spiritual awareness, and Ausar, which means born of Aset, is depicted as a bull. He represents the resurrected man and is judge of the dead.

2. BCE: Before the Common Era, an alternative for BC - Before Christ. CE represents the Common Era, or AD.

Chapter 2

The Giza - Genesis Connection

Joseph died at the age of one hundred and ten. He was embalmed
and laid to rest in a coffin in Egypt.

— Genesis 50:26

Who created the earth in six days, and what was the significance of the seventh day? Is this the prime number in a complex set of lineages and star maps? Who really wrote Genesis, the blueprint of our civilization, and who – what — is buried under the Giza Plateau? What on earth has all of this to do with many ancient mythological gods?

We are rapidly approaching a cosmic watershed that will not only completely alter the concept of one's beliefs of the evolution of man on this planet Terra, but our true origins in the cosmos as a whole. Were we in fact derived from "itinerants" in the galaxies, searching out suitable planets to establish a genetic stock? How were our solar system and the planets originally formed — and who or what intervened in our genetic evolution?

In order to establish an appropriate mind-set or perception for understanding our thesis with greater clarity, first it is important to realize, as posed above in our set of questions, that we are not talking merely about "Earth's history" and life on Planet Earth, but rather, cosmic history and cosmic life, of which our galaxy, solar system and planet are only a part – albeit, an important one.

Thus, in interpreting the Book of Genesis from a cosmic stance, we are not merely talking about human life beginning here on Earth, but a "seeding" of this planet Earth by other beings who came from other places in the cosmos.

In the Book of Genesis, God commanded Jacob to "spread abroad, to the west, and to the east, and to the north, and to the south . . . And in these and in thy seed shall all the families of the earth be blessed . . ." (28:14).

Thus, Jacob had been bringing in people from other *worlds* who had already gone through the growth process that we here on Earth are about to experience. Ultimately, Jacob integrated these people into becoming a group that believed in free will, and One God.

Through well-recognized and extensive Remote Viewing work dealing with so-called "fossilized spirits," we have learned that the Pleiades is the (our) Sun's "lineage" or line of descent, whereas the Orion and Sirian lineages are the Tigris and Euphrates, respectively.

Once Jacob decides to re-locate those people who believe in One God into the Pleiades lineage (his home lineage) on Earth, he must first alter the DNA to suit the New World as one set or race of peoples. Also, since he was descended from the Sirian line, he must then "cross over." This move will take him out of the Sirian line (Euphrates) and force him to make a deal with the Orions and Pleiadians.The Pleiadians are the main lineage or line of descent, and the Orions (Tigris) are the third line of descent.

This is why the well-known cry, "Let My People Go!" is so relevant. It is this race of people (the Pleiadians) that is brought here to Planet Earth with Jacob — whose name changes to Israel, because the context has also changed. This point is also borne out, as we will see later in the book, in the connection of the Betel-HAM (Bethlehem) SETH-SHEM and JAPETH-JARED lineage. It is this association that supports the three lineages.

The deal is ultimately struck and one-half of the people, those who possessed tails, (Orions, who are reptilians) are sent ahead. The second half (the Pleiadians) are brought in with Jacob as they cross the Euphrates. These are the people who will inhabit the New World. DNA alterations are then made and the reptilian tails are permanently removed. Thus, both the Pleiadian and Orion interests are satisfied.

To support this information, we read in Genesis (Chapter 30: 32) that Jacob takes the animals of all colors, fencing them off. This was to integrate all the "DNA processing" and is a method similar to the one we use today in genetic experimentation, when we select the stronger and more complete animal.

We read in Genesis 32:8 about this integration of the Orion lineage (the "reptilian" factor) with the Syrian ("Humanoid") lineage:

Then Jacob was greatly afraid and distressed; and he divided
the people that were with him, and the flocks and
herds and camels, into two companies

At this point. Jacob meets the "angel." He crosses the Euphrates River and meets an angel, a Pleiadian, with whom he "wrestles" until he loses his "tail." He is now renamed and is no longer spoken of as "Jacob." That is, he becomes "Israel," or the earth in its present position.

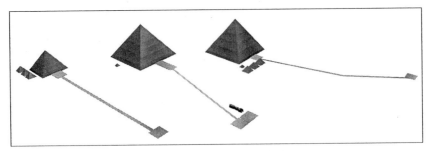

Figure 2.1 — Aerial Model of Plateau

ARE WE APPROACHING ANOTHER "FIRST TIME"?

"Earth changes" today is a byword for earthquakes, volcanic activity, severe extreme weather and maximum solar flare activity. Are these events a precursor to the ultimate event known in the Bible as Armageddon — a time when a conflict occurs to regain the soul rights? This is the scenario of enslavement versus ascension or liberation. Is it a time of harvest, when a race, or several races, are due to return to earth in order to repossess what they understood to be originally and rightfully theirs? Is it a return of what the ancient Egyptians termed the "Zep Tepi," The First Time — a time that began with the gods of the primeval ocean (Nun), proceeded to Horus[2] and the redemption of Osiris, god of the underworld, and led finally to resurrection? With the underworld in the present state of evolution, if one follows "Osiris," is this the time when we pass through to the upper level on the ladder of progression, or, vertical ascension, where Osiris is equated with Jacob (Jacob's ladder)?

The ancient Egyptians considered this period a "time of the gods"; an actual historical event believed to have been recorded in the heavens above. It is also an event that was continually re-enacted in the cosmos, seen as reflected in the displays of the celestial orbs and constellations, where the main "characters" were such "gods" as Re (the sun), Osiris (Orion), Isis (Sirius) and Thoth the moon, to name but a few.

The Giza Plateau is the crux of this whole affair, and using this most ancient of sites, we will endeavor to offer an explanation and correlation to the events we are witnessing today.

It is important to bear in mind that the whole background and interpretation of Genesis is one of the most complex sets of data instigated. It is data that not only demonstrates the blueprint of humankind, but also deals with the physical laws of nature.

The "actors" in the texts have remarkable similarities to the "myths" of many other civilizations, especially those of ancient Egypt. Here we find our original base, the city of Babel[1] and the resulting diversification of cultures and societies.

Are these stories of Genesis merely a re-enactment of earlier myths equated by synonyms of our players, such as Osiris, Seth (Set), Horus and Isis? Indeed, is the time drawing near for the return of the Zep Tepi – "The First Time"?

This possibility can be explained if in fact, in alignment with our theme, other races were "lifted" and placed here after the last ascension, arriving on this world from various other worlds in the cosmos. Those still in possession of a physical body at the time, came together to prepare the planet, from which followed the Babel scenario.

Once the immediate need was met on this planet, it was then that the differences began to emerge, resulting in a cultural split within the diversity of races. Diverse cultures leading to many different beliefs would account for the different names for the one and same God. This could also be equated with the Adam and Eve and the "Garden of Eden" scenario. An apple tree may have many branches and apples, but all originate from the same tree, the same root.

Genesis, the source text that we are using for our thesis, is the most complex, interwoven coded piece of literature ever written. What we present here are only a few of many conclusions derived from several levels of this ancient work.

One of the latter levels of this work reveals man's genetic code, both in structure as well as operational interaction of its functional mechanism. The initial level, proven to a minimum of its fifth Decimal Point, deals with inter-dimensional physics and as this is both testable and measurable, we will use this as the base level from which we will present our findings.

At this point, we were able to definitively conclude that whoever wrote the book of Genesis had either constructed the pyramid complex at the Giza Plateau, and/or possessed intimate knowledge of the blueprint from which the pyramid complex was erected.

We will now trace the relevant sections of Genesis explaining each part as related to the mathematics and lineage of the planet earth.

THE MATHEMATICS OF GENESIS AS RELATED TO THE LINEAGE OF THE PLANET EARTH

Planet Earth was conceived by two sets of lineage: first, the solar sun, and second, the mathematical set of the six identified in the Bible as Adam, Seth, Enosh, Cain, Mahalaleel and Jared. Adam would be our point of origin in our "star map" and therefore would be established at zero degrees in the "Garden of Eden." Nahor then becomes the father of Terah.

> Genesis 11:24
>
> *When Nahor had lived twenty-nine years, he became the father of Terah; Terah became the father of Abram, (Teran), Nahor (Orion) and Haran (Sirian).*

> Genesis 11:26
>
> *When Terah had lived seventy years, (7-70) he became the father of Abram, (Pleiadian lineage) Nahor, (70) and Haran (700).*

Later, we will explain the tree of life and its various branches, and the eating of the apples as a synonym for the different worlds or apples — same tree, different apples.

A sharp shift now occurs, from the flow that began at Genesis 1:1 and walked us through the workings of universal physics; terminating at our three lineage lines.

In lineage one, Terah represents Adam, our sun. Abram and his lineage are traced back through the Pleiades system (in the constellation of Taurus) from the star Alcyone. "Adam" gives birth to "Abram"; Abram then gives birth to the earth or "Abraham."

In lineage two, Haran is the product of the Jared lineage, Chaldeon or "Nordic," and is associated with the river Euphrates; whereas lineage three, Nahor, is the product of the Seth lineage (reptilian) and associated with the river Tigris.

Seth (or Set) was the patron deity of Lower (Northern) Egypt, and represented the fierce storms of the desert that the Lower Egyptians sought to appease. However, when Upper Egypt conquered Lower Egypt and ushered in the 1st Dynasty, Set became known as the evil enemy of Horus (Upper Egypt's dynastic god) and was represented by a big-eared imaginary animal with red hair resembling a donkey. In ancient Egypt, color was an integral part of the substance and being of everything in life. The color of something was a clue to the substance or heart of the matter, and in this case, the color red was the color of life and of victory.

It was Seth and his 72 conspirators who murdered Osiris (his brother). Then they threw the coffin in which Osiris was murdered, into the Nile with his divine body still inside. Isis, with the help of her sister Nephthys, and Anubis and Thoth, magically located Osiris's body. However, on learning that his brother's body was found, Seth tore it into fourteen pieces and scattered them throughout Egypt. Isis once again found every part of his body, except for his phallus, which had been eaten by the now-cursed Nile fish. She magically re-assembled Osiris and resurrected him long enough to be impregnated by him so that she could give birth to the new king, Horus.

We now come to Lot, who is equated with lineage number three, the last battle of the last time. (Abram is lineage number one.) Thus, Earth is in the location of lineage number one, where Mercury is now in its present position.

> Genesis 11:29
>> *Abram and Nahor took wives; the name of Abram's wife was Sar'ai, (lineage one and two) and the name of Nahor's wife, Milcah, daughter of Haran the father of Milcah and Iscah (lineage two and three).*

> Genesis 12:1
>> *The Lord said to Abram, "Go forth from the land of your kinsfolk and from your father's house to a land that I will show you."*

Thus Earth is born from the sun, and in Genesis 12:3, Eve is extracted from the sun's rib, mother earth.

> Genesis 12:4
>> *Abram went as the Lord directed him; and Lot went with him. Abram was seventy-five years old when he left Haran.*

ALIEN INTERVENTION

> Genesis 15:13
>> *Then the Lord said to Abram, "Know for certain that your descendants shall be aliens in a land not their own, where they shall be enslaved and oppressed for four hundred years."*

The word "aliens" in this case would be the people now without a home, and the time of oppression for 400 years would be the point where the complete set of three arrives, including those of the ascension — thus, coming around in a complete full circle.

Genesis 15:14

> But I will bring judgment on the nation they must serve, and in the end they will depart with great wealth. [Ascension achieved.]

Genesis 15:15

> You, however, shall join your forefathers in peace; you shall be buried at a contented old age.

Genesis 15:16

> In the fourth time-span the others shall come back here; the wickedness of the Amorites will not have reached its full measure until then." [at this time and space]

One must bear in mind this "fourth generation" that is completed once the earth reaches the present location of Mars at 1000 or "zero" degrees. As in "revelation," the "1000 year reign" or the 13th Baktun, 13 degrees to the inside from the point of origin (see 17:18 below) is the four time-spans of 100 years apiece.

Comet Lee therefore signified the fourth time-span immediately after the recent solar eclipse of 1999, as it demonstrated the beginning of the time leading into the fourth time-span, or the events leading into the final date of December 21, 2012.

Genesis 15:17

> When the sun had set and it was dark, there appeared a smoking brazier and a flaming torch, which passed between those two pieces [where the resulting Electromagnetic field produced by the Comet coincides with the "end time"].

COMET LEE

Comet Lee, known as COMET C/1999 H1 (Lee) and in some circles referred to as the "Nostradamus Comet" (Ervin[3] 2000) was first reported on April 16,1999 as a visual discovery by Steven Lee during a star party near Mudgee, New South

Wales, Australia.

The comet was described as 9th magnitude, diffuse and having no tail. By May, 1999, it was visible in both hemispheres and in mid-August emerged from the solar glare to become a Northern Hemisphere circumpolar object. In September, it slowly faded out. However, due to the build-up at that time of increasing solar activity, such as solar flares and Coronal Mass Ejections, Lee was subject to alterations of orbit, thus bringing it nearer to earth.

The Abram lineage is the first one and Hagar is lineage number two. Thus, Ishmael is a "wild man."

Genesis 16:11

> *Besides, the Lord's messenger said to her of the LORD, "You are now pregnant and shall bear a son; you shall name him Ishmael, for the Lord has heard you, God has answered you.*

Genesis 16:12

> *"He shall be a wild ass of a man, his hand against everyone, and everyone's hand against him; in opposition to all his kin shall he encamp."*

Genesis 17:5

> *"No longer shall you be called Abram; your name shall be Abraham, for I am making you father of a host of nations."*

In other words, God is speaking of many nations and many worlds, where people, i.e., those of the "covenant," would be brought together after the last ascension.

Genesis 17:6

> *"I will render you exceedingly fertile; I will make nations of you; kings shall stem from you."*

Genesis 17:7

> *"I will maintain my covenant with you and your descendants after you throughout the ages as an everlasting pact."*

Genesis 17:8

> *"I will give to you, and to your descendants after you the land in which you are now staying, the whole land of , as a permanent possession; and I will be their God."*

ON THE EIGHTH DAY[4]

"Heaven and earth were made in six days." The seventh day was one of rest; thus, the eighth day[4] was the very first day of existence. It is at this point where the reptilian form is "lost" (the skin is shed).

Genesis 17:9

> *God also said to Abraham, "On your part, you and your descen-dants after you must keep my covenant throughout the ages."*

Genesis 17:10

> *"This is my covenant with you and your descendants after you that you must keep: every male among you shall be circumcised."*

Genesis 17:11

> *"Circumcise the flesh of your foreskin, and that shall be the mark of the covenant between you and me."*

Genesis 17:12

> *"Throughout the ages, every male among you, when he is eight days old, shall be circumcised, including houseborn slaves and those acquired with money from any foreigner who is not of your blood."*

Genesis 17:13

> *"Yes, both the houseborn slaves and those acquired with money must be circumcised. Thus my covenant shall be your flesh as an everlasting pact."*

Genesis 17:14

> *"If a male is uncircumcised, that is, if the flesh of his foreskin has not been cut away, such a one shall be cut off from his people; he has broken my covenant."*

SARAI TO SARAH

Genesis 17:15

> *God further said to Abraham: "As for your wife Sarai, do not call her Sarai; her name shall be Sarah."*

Figure 2.2 — Three-Star Crop Circle, Wiltshire

ISAAC

At the time of Isaac's birth, Abraham was 100 = 1 # 0 - 0 an Sarah (Isis) at the time of birth was 90 = 30 # 30 # 30.

Recently, we observed a crop circle[5] in Wiltshire UK, where three stars are seen to be within a circle. Very soon, these formations should demonstrate to us these stars materializing into one as we move forwards to the alignment event on December 21, 2012.

Genesis 17:18

> *Then Abraham said to God, "Let but Ishmael live on by your favor."*

It is this stage where this race shed its skin, Abraham at "99" turning 100; Ishmael at 13 (degrees), which equates to Baktun, the end of the cycle.

Genesis 17:23

> *Then Abraham took his son Ish'mael and all his slaves, whether born in his house or acquired with his money – every male among the members of Abraham's household – and he circumcised the flesh of their foreskins on that same day.*

Genesis 17:24

> *Abraham was ninety-nine years old when the flesh of his foreskin was circumcised.*

Genesis 17:25

> *And his son, Ishmael was thirteen years old when the flesh of his foreskin was circumcised.*

Genesis 17:26

> *Thus, on that same day Abraham and his son Ishmael were circumcised.*

The three wise men, the High Council, receive gifts such as food. Could these be the three representatives from the three lineages? That is, the Orion, Pleiades and Syrian lineages, where the representatives are promised the future harvest, now soon to unfold? Those available to be harvested will be those who choose to remain, since their lack of commitment to the covenant, as established by the one God, has not been kept; and thus will hold them back on ascension this time around.

As we have been told, the "three wise men" offered the three gifts of Gold (or rock – see Exodus chapter), Frankincense and Myrrh. Gold (rock) may be equated to our planet. Frankincense may be thought of as representative of our DNA, and the herb Myrrh, may be considered the plant connection. Together, they constitute the whole of our planetary and evolutionary make-up.

This same situation arose at the previous end time in relation to the planet Mars, where we were located prior to Planet Earth, as was noted by the absence of people. When this end time period came, war ensued over the conflict of souls on Mars, since the deal on that planet was exactly the same as the deal made on Planet Earth.

As history repeats itself, this will occur once more on our planet. However, on this occasion it is hoped that many more will ascend.

Genesis 18:2

> *Looking up, he saw three men standing nearby. When he saw them, he ran from the entrance of the tent to greet them; and bowed to the ground.*

Abraham was informed that the "Lord" will return after the birth. This "birth" event we believe will be witnessed on December 21, 2000, and we will return to this point later in the book.

Genesis 18:14

> *"Is anything too marvelous for the Lord to do? At this appointed time, about this time next year, I will return to you, and Sarah will have a son."*

It is at this point that Ephraim will make his appearance, upon which time the rose is passed on (or as we mentioned previously, Frankincense, where it relates to his people). Ephraim then takes on the responsibility of leading his people.

The burial site of Sarah here is the "Hall of Records," the location of which was bought and paid for 400 shekels = 0, 0, 0.

DESCRIPTION AND LOCATION OF THE HALL OF RECORDS (HOR)

Genesis 23:4

> *"Although I am a resident alien among you, sell me from your holdings a piece of property for a burial ground, that I may bury my dead wife."*

Genesis 23:9

> *"To sell me the cave of Machpelah that he owns; it is at the edge of his field. Let him sell it to me in your presence, at its full price, for a burial place."*

Genesis 23:11

> *"Please sir, listen to me! I give you both the field and the cave in it; in the presence of my kinsman I make this gift. Bury your dead!"*

Genesis 23:15

"Sir, listen to me! A piece of land worth four hundred shekels of silver — what is that between you and me, as long as you can bury your dead!"

Genesis 23:19

After this transaction, Abraham buried his wife Sarah in the cave of the field of Machpelah, facing Mamre (Hebron) in the land of .

Genesis 23:20

Thus the field with its cave was transferred from the Hittites to Abraham as a burial place.

Abraham is Buried Next to Sarah in the Hall of Records

Genesis 25:10

The field that Abraham had bought from the Hittites; there he was buried next to his wife Sarah.

The Older will Serve the Younger

Genesis 25:23

. . . and he answered her: "Two nations are in your womb, two peoples are quarrelling while still within you; But one shall surpass the other, and the older shall serve the younger."

Esau, the eldest, was one nation, who was and remains of the reptilian race; and the youngest, Jacob, was the second nation.

Isaac was 60 years old (60 degrees) and still possessed the vestige of a reptilian tail. The gravesite of Isaac is the same as that of Osiris.

Genesis 25:24

When the time of her delivery came, there were twins in her womb.

Genesis 25:25

The first to emerge was reddish, and his whole body was like a hairy mantle; so they named him Esau.

Genesis 25:26

> *His brother came out next, gripping Esau's heel; so they named*
> *him Jacob. Isaac was sixty years old when they were born.*

Joseph stays close to his "tents" (tombs) on the plateau and from there
acquires his birthright from Esau. Isaac's death ended Earth's placement at the
Mercury stage. Earth then moved onto its next location, where Venus now sits.

Genesis 25:30

> *He said to Jacob, "Let me gulp down some of that red stuff;*
> *I'm starving." (That is why he was called Edom.)*

Genesis 25:31

> *But Jacob replied, "First give me your birthright in exchange for it."*

Genesis 25:32

> *"Look," said Esau, "I'm on the point of dying. What good will*
> *any birthright do me?"*

Genesis 25:34

> *Jacob then gave him some bread and the lentil stew; and Esau ate,*
> *drank, got up, and went his way. Esau cared little for his birthright.*

Isaac now seals the pact, thus ensuring peace and so retaining control on
the plateau.

Genesis 26:24

> *The same night the Lord appeared to him and said: "I AM the*
> *God of your father Abraham. You have no need to fear; since I*
> *am with you, I will bless you and multiply your descendants*
> *for the sake of my servant Abraham."*

Genesis 26:25

> *So he built an altar there and invoked the Lord by name. After he*
> *had pitched his tent there, his servants began to dig a well nearby.*

Genesis 26:26

> *Abimelech had meanwhile come to him from Gerar,*
> *accompanied by Ahuzzath, his councillor, and Phicol, the*
> *general of his army.*

Genesis 26:27

> *Isaac asked them, "Why have you come to see me, seeing that*
> *you hate me and have driven me away from you?"*

Genesis 26:28

> *They answered: "We are convinced that the Lord is with you,*
> *so we propose that there be a sworn agreement between our*
> *two sides – between you and us."*

Genesis 26:29

> *"You shall not act unkindly toward us, just as we have not*
> *molested you, but have always acted kindly towards you and*
> *have let you depart in peace. Henceforth, 'The Lord's blessing*
> *be upon you!' "*

Genesis 26:30

> *Isaac then made a feast for them, and they ate and drank.*

Genesis 26:31

> *Early next morning they exchanged oaths. Then Isaac bade*
> *them farewell, and they departed from him in peace.*

Jacob now steals Isaac's blessing, giving him possession of all that is above ground, while Esau is blessed but must dwell below ground; simultaneously serving his brother until at such time he "becomes restive."

Jacob is now introduced to what we call our satellite, the moon, where the "step towers" were constructed, (Jacob's ladder) or what we now term, "monoliths."

It is interesting to note that from a conversation with Dr. Boylan[6] and Dr. Wolf, (NSA advisor) that the NSC consultant mentioned an extraterrestrial space beacon, dubbed "the Monolith," which had been retrieved from space in 1972 by a U.S. military spacecraft and brought back to Earth for study. The beacon looks somewhat like, but is smaller than the monolith in the movie *2001*.[7]

As a matter of relevance, we thought it essential to extract a portion of this article:[8]

The MJ-12 scientific section began analysis of this beacon at RCA's underwater laboratory north of Abaco Island, Bahamas. The military, naturally, wanted to examine the beacon's intense power source for possible conversion to weapons application. The Monolith's extremely powerful energy fields were designed for its precise position in deep space.

When it was brought to Earth, those fields exerted an unbalancing force. Dr. Wolf said, "I told them not to keep it. Already the Moon is 2% out of its orbit." This has adversely affected the weather and global warming. "I told them [MJ-12 subcommittee] to get it the hell off of Earth!" He has been negotiating with U.S. National Security officials visiting him about returning the space beacon to its former position in space and restoring the balance. As leverage, he has delivered an ultimatum, threatening to stop participating in the Acclimation Program, and stop serving as the premiere ET-specialist consultant to the National Security Council.[8] His final trump argument to the NSC has been, "I will blow the whistle publicly on the whole thing," if the space beacon is not put back. He is so serious about this matter that he contemplated asking the Director of the Secret Service to provide a Secret Service detail, or asking his Admiral colleague on the NSC's MJ-12 subcommittee to provide a Navy SEAL contingent, to accompany the previously-mentioned female UN Security Council official to Area 51 to compel the return of the Monolith.

Figure 2.3 — Low Resolution Screenshot from NASA VRML

Wolf also stated, "We are currently negotiating with an ET mothership to bring the Moon back into its axis." He declared that the Moon is artificial, long ago positioned in its orbit by extraterrestrials. Furthermore, he confirmed that there is an extraterrestrial base on the Moon. When I suggested the base was on the dark side, he did not challenge that assumption.

Similar monoliths are located on the Moon's surface, acting as relay boosters to aid in the harvesting and recycling of the energy of souls from planet earth. The working equipment of these monoliths may be found below the Giza plateau.

> Genesis 28:10
>
> *Jacob departed from Beer-sheba, and proceeded toward Haran.*

> Genesis 28:11
>
> *When he came upon a certain shrine, as the sun had already set, he stopped there for the night. Taking one of the stones at the shrine, he put it under his head and lay down to sleep at that spot.*

> Genesis 28:12
>
> *Then he had a dream: A stairway rested on the ground, with its top reaching to the heavens; and God's messengers were going up and down on it.*

> Genesis 28:13
>
> *And there was the Lord standing beside him and saying, "I, the Lord, am the God of your forefather Abraham and the God of Isaac: The land on which you are lying I will give to you and your descendants."*

> Genesis 28:14
>
> *"These shall be plentiful as the dust of the earth and through them you shall spread out east and west, north and south. In you and your descendants all the nations of the earth shall find blessing."*

> Genesis 28:15
>
> *Know that I am with you: I will protect you wherever you go and bring you back to this land. I will never leave you until I have done what I promised."*

Genesis 28:16

> *When Jacob awoke from his sleep, he exclaimed, "Truly, the Lord is in this spot, although I did not know it!"*

Genesis 28:17

> *In solemn wonder he cried out: "How awesome is this shrine! This is nothing else but an abode of God, and that is the gateway to heaven!"*

Genesis 28:18

> *Early the next morning Jacob took the stone that he had put under his head, set it up as a memorial stone, and poured oil on top of it.*

Genesis 28:19

> *He called that site Bethle, whereas the former name of the town had been Luz.*

GENESIS CHAPTERS 29-31

Jacob now leaves Isaac and goes to Haran (Chaldeans) where he meets Laban, son of Nahor and of the reptilian race. Jacob wants to marry Rachel, but Leah, her older sister, is unwed. Consequently, Nohor makes him labor seven years to wed Leah first, and another seven years in order to finally wed Rachel as well. Directly after this time, Joseph is born. For six more years the breeding is different and stronger, as a manipulated form of genetics; 20 years is mentioned twice. In other words, 7-7-6: where Mercury is at 7, Venus is at 6, and earth is about to move to present location at 7.

Genesis 31:41

> *Of the twenty years that I have now spent in your household, I slaved fourteen years for your two daughters and six years for your flock, while you changed my wages time after time.*

Here we are talking about the three stages of our sun: Adam, Abram and Abraham; the ancestral god of Abraham (Pleiadian); and the "awesome one" of Isaac.

Isaac represents the Earth when born from Abraham, thus placing Earth in the position that is presently occupied by the planet Mercury. This then relates to the Earth in its second stage of development, where Venus is presently located, and is referred to as Jacob. Earth's present position is represented (in this lineage) as Joseph, and Earth's geometric zero degree is the sun.

So, Isaac is 7, Jacob, 70 and Joseph, 700.

Genesis 31:42

> *If my ancestral God, the God of Abraham and the Awesome One of Isaac, had not been on my side, you would now have sent me away empty-handed. But God saw my plight and the fruits of my toil, and last night he gave judgement.*

We now come to the mountain of stone, Jacob and Laban, and tomb number one, today known as the pyramid of Menkaura. Jacob takes the oath by the awesome one of Isaac.

Genesis 31:45

> *Then Jacob took a stone, and set it up as a memorial stone.*

Genesis 31:46

> *Jacob said to his kinsmen, "Gather some stones." So they got some stones, and made a mound; and they had a meal there at the mound.*

Genesis 31:52

> *This ground shall be witness, and that this memorial stone shall be witness, that, with hostile intent, neither may I pass beyond this mound into your territory, nor may you pass beyond it into mine.*

GENESIS - CHAPTER 32

We now come to a relevant portion of the text, which may be current with events about to presently unfold: The meeting of God's messengers at his encampment on the Giza Plateau.

Genesis 32:1

> *Early the next morning, Laban kissed his grandchildren and his daughters goodbye: then he set out on his journey back home.*

Genesis 32: 2

> *While Jacob continued on his own way, then God's messengers encountered Jacob.*

Genesis 32:3

> *When he saw them he said, "This is God's encampment."*
> *So he named that place Mahanaim.*

At this point Esau comes to meet Jacob with 400 men; Jacob then divides the camp into two, that is, the division of the reptilian and human life forms.

Genesis 32:7

> *When the messengers returned to Jacob, they said, "We reached*
> *your brother Esau. He is now coming to meet you, accompanied*
> *by four hundred men."*

Jacob sends half of the camp ahead to Esau who was on Mars, in its present position. Before the move, however, Jacob does not go with Esau and returns to the place where Isaac is (our present Earth) at the time of Earth's move to its present location.

Genesis 32:8

> *Jacob was very much frightened. In his anxiety, he divided the*
> *people who were with him, as well as his flocks, herds and camels,*
> *into two camps.*

Genesis 32:9

> *"If Esau should attack and overwhelm one camp," he reasoned,*
> *"the remaining camp may still survive."*

At this point, Jacob meets the "angel' across the Euphrates. Jacob crosses a river, possibly the Euphrates, and meets an angel, a Pleiadian, with whom he "wrestles" until Jacob loses his "tail." He is now renamed and no longer spoken of as "Jacob," but becomes "Israel," or Earth in its present position.

Genesis 32:23

> *In the course of that night, however, Jacob arose, took his two*
> *wives, with the two maidservants and his eleven children, and*
> *crossed the ford of the Jabbok.*

Genesis 32:25

> *Jacob was left there alone. Then some man wrestled with him until the break of the dawn.*

Genesis 32:25

> *When the man saw that he could not prevail him, he struck Jacob's hip at its socket, so that the hip socket was wrenched as they wrestled.*

Genesis 32:28

> *"What is your name?" the man asked. He answered "Jacob."*

Genesis 32:29

> *Then the man said, "You shall no longer be spoken of as Jacob, but as Israel, because you have contended with divine human beings and prevailed."*

Genesis 32:30

> *Jacob then asked him, "Do tell me your name please." He answered, "Why should you want to know my name?" With that he bade him farewell.*

Genesis 32:31

> *Jacob named the place Penuel, "because I have seen God face to face," he said, "yet my life has been spared."*

Genesis 32:32

> *At sunrise, as he left Penuel, Jacob limped along because of his hip.*

Genesis 32:33

> *That is why, to this day, the Israelites do not eat the sciatic muscle that is on the hip socket, inasmuch as Jacob's hip socket was struck at the sciatic muscle.*

Canaan pitches his "tent" and sets up a memorial stone and altar to 'El-El'ohe (the god of) Israel.

Genesis 33:18

> *And Jacob came safely to the city of Shechem, which is in the land of , on his way from Paddan-aram; and he camped before the city.*

Genesis 33:19

> *And from the sons of Hamor, Shechem's father, he bought for a hundred pieces of money the piece of land on which he had pitched his tent.*

Genesis 33:20

> *There he erected an altar and called it El-El'ohe-Israel.*

GENESIS - CHAPTER 35

Jacob is now instructed to construct an altar at "Bethel," adjacent to the site of Menkaura (Laban's site). This is "tomb" number two, in position near and under what is known today as the pyramid of Khafre. God then gives Jacob the lands and rights that had previously belonged to Abraham and Isaac – i.e., Bethel, or the Giza Plateau.

Genesis 35:1

> *God said to Jacob, "Arise, go up to Bethel, and dwell there; and make there an altar to the God who appeared to you when you fled from your brother Esau."*

Genesis 35:10

> *And God said to him, "Your name is Jacob; no longer shall your name be called Jacob, Israel shall be your name." So his name was called Israel.*

Genesis 35:11

> *And God said to him, "I am God Almighty: be fruitful and multiply; a nation and a company of nations shall come from you, and kings shall spring from you."*

Genesis 35:12

> *"The land which I gave to Abraham and Isaac I will give to you, and I will give the land to your descendants after you."*

Rachel gives birth to Benjamin and dies. Joseph builds a monument to her and marks her grave with a pyramid on the plateau, possibly the satellite pyramid of Khafre's pyramid.

Genesis 35:17
> *And when she was in her hard labor, the midwife said to her, "Fear not; for now you will have another son."*

Genesis 35:18
> *And as her soul was departing (for she died), she called his name Ben-o'ni; but his father called his name Benjamin.*

Genesis 35:19
> *So Rachel died, and she was buried on the way to Ephrath (that is, Bethlehem).*

Genesis 35:20
> *and Jacob set up a pillar upon her grave; it is the pillar of Rachel's tomb, which is there to this day.*

Genesis 35:21
> *Israel journeyed on, and pitched his tent beyond the tower of Eder.*

Isaac dies at 180 years and Esau and Jacob bury him in tomb number one on the Giza Plateau.

Figure 2.4 —Pyramid of Menkaure

Genesis 35:28
> *The lifetime of Isaac was one hundred and eighty years; then he breathed his last.*

Genesis 35:29

> *After a full life, he died as an old man and was taken to his*
> *kinsmen. His sons Esau and Jacob buried him.*

It must be remembered that all monuments, excluding Abraham's and the Hall of Records, already existed. They were erected at Bethel (the Giza Plateau) which is now sitting where the moon is in Earth's present position. Up until that time the reptilian souls were not re-cycled, since the genetic input was not coded into the "soul" machine. However, it seems that they are still endeavouring to interbreed with humans in an attempt to acquire the souls into a re-cycle pattern. The reptilian DNA is considered to be a borderline RNA (Ribose Nucleic Acid), the DNA combination.

GENESIS - CHAPTER 36:

Esau now departs for the highlands, Se'ir, or Mars, as we know it, and Joseph stays here on earth, at Bethel, the Plateau (Canaan). Esau and his 400 men came originally from Se'ir when they met Jacob.

Genesis 36:7

> *Their possessions had become too great for them to dwell*
> *together, and the land in which they were staying could not*
> *support because of their livestock.*

Genesis 36:8

> *So Esau settled in the highlands of Seir. (Esau is Edom.)*

GENESIS - CHAPTER 41

Joseph marries As'enath, daughter of Poti'phera, priest of ON, (Iunu in Coptic and Biblical terms) and known today as Heliopolis, a suburb of Cairo. Here is where the important temples of the sun god Re were situated — Re-atum, the creator god and Re-Harakhty.

Genesis 41:45

> *Pharaoh also bestowed the name of Zaph'enath-pane'ah on*
> *Joseph and he gave him in marriage As'enath, the daughter*
> *of Poti'phera, priest of Heliopolis.*

GENESIS - CHAPTER 49 - JACOB'S TESTAMENT

Genesis 49:22

> *Joseph is a wild colt, a wild colt by a spring, a wild ass on a hillside.*

Genesis 49:23

> *Harrying and attacking, the archers opposed him.*

Genesis 49:24

> *But each one's bow remained stiff, as their arms were unsteady, by the power of the Mighty One of Jacob, because of the shepherd, the rock of Israel.*

Genesis 49:25

> *The god of your father, who helps you, God Almighty, who blesses you, With the blessings of the heavens above, the blessings of the abyss that crouches below, the blessings of breasts and womb.*

Genesis 49:26

> *The blessings of fresh grain and blossoms, the blessings of the everlasting mountains, the delights of the eternal hills. May they rest on the head of Joseph, on the brow of the prince among his brothers.*

The verse below concerns Benjamin (Thoth) and the description of the process whereby the collection and re-distribution of souls is carried out. Thoth, whose animal was an Ibis or dog-headed baboon, was an ancient Egyptian deity, and the original Ogdoad of Hermopolis were called "the souls of Thoth." Thoth was created by the power of utterance and was called the inventor of speech. He was said to have been "self-begotten," having appeared at the dawn of time on a lotus flower. One of his greatest services to Re was the retrieval of his eye, and as a reward, Re created the moon for Thoth. He was also called the "measurer of time" and said to be inventor of mathematics, astronomy and engineering. As such, he was the accountant to the gods and the secretary of Re.

It is said his silver boat transported the souls of the dead across the night sky.

Genesis 49:27

> *Benjamin is a ravenous wolf; mornings he devours the prey, and evenings he distributes the spoil.*

Jacob and his last days, on the Giza Plateau:

Genesis 49:28

> *All these are the twelve tribes of Israel, and this is what their father spoke about to them, as he bade an appropriate message.*

Genesis 49:29

> *Then he gave then this charge: "Since I am about to be taken to my kindred, bury me with my fathers in the cave that lies in the field of Ephron, the Hittite.*

Genesis 49:30

> *The cave in the field of Machpelah, facing on Mamre, in the land of, the field that Abraham bought from Ephron the Hittite for a burial ground.*

Genesis 49:31

> *There Abraham and his wife Sarah are buried, and so too are Isaac and his wife Rebekah, and there too, I buried Leah.*

Genesis 49:32

> *The field and the cave in it had been purchased from the Hittites.*

Genesis 49:33

> *When Jacob had finished giving these instructions to his sons, he drew up his feet into the bed, breathed his last, and was taken to his kindred.*

Genesis - Chapter 50

Joseph buries Jacob in tomb number two.

Figure 2.5 — Pyramids of Menkaure, Khafre and Khufu

Genesis 50:5

> *"My father made me swear, saying, 'I am about to die: in my tomb which I hewed out for myself in the land of , there shall you bury me.' Now therefore let me go up, I pray you, and bury my father; then I will return."*

Joseph now dies at 110 years. They embalm him (preserved in some form of suspended animation process in order to return at some future date) and place him in a coffin. There is no mention of burial!

Genesis 50:20

> *Even though you meant harm to me, God meant it for good, to achieve his present end, the survival of many people.*

Genesis 50:24

> *Joseph said to his brothers, "I am about to die. God will surely take care of you and lead you out of this land that he promised on oath to Abraham, Isaac and Jacob."*

Genesis 50:25

> *Then putting the sons of Israel under oath, he continued, "When God thus takes care of you, you must bring my bones up with you from this place."*

Genesis 50:26

> *So Joseph died, being a hundred and ten. He was embalmed*
> *and laid to rest in a coffin in Egypt.*

The above passages seem to indicate that Joseph was "embalmed" or preserved in order to remain in "suspended animation" until such time that he is awakened.

Figure 2.6 — Pyramid of Khufu

Notes

1.   Babel: The "Tower of Babel" is the name of the building mentioned in Genesis 11:1-9.

2.   Horus: Also known as Hor-akhuti (Horus of the Horizons), Hor-behedet, Hadit, Hor-pa-kraat (Horus the Child), Her-ur (Horus the Elder), Ra-Hoor-Khuit. The symbol is a falcon, the Eye of Horus while the usual image is that of a human with the head of a falcon, and was considered one of the most important deities of Egypt. Horus is a mixture of the original deities known as "Horus the Child" and "Horus the Elder". As the Child, Horus is the son of Osiris and Isis, who, upon reaching adulthood, becomes known as Her-nedj-tef-ef ("Horus, Avenger of His Father") by avenging his father's death, by defeating and casting out his evil uncle Horus had four sons, *Amse, Duamutef, Hapi, Qebhsenuef*

3.   Colonel James B. Ervin: COMET C/1999 H1 (Lee) = NOSTRADAMUS COMET ?
     A web article that appeared on the Millennium science group web site on 10th June 1999
     http://www.millenngroup.com/repository/cometary/ervin1.htm

4.   On the Eighth Day. One of our recent Ambilac web site articles, where we explained the symbolism of the "Eight days" in connection with the Fatima prophecy. "Seven months out from May brings us to December, eight days out from the 13th brings us to the 21st December. In all our articles we refer to the 'End Count' date of December 21st 2012".

5.   Crop circles. The "star" crop circle consisted of a large round circle with three star shapes within that circle. It appeared in August 2000, in Wiltshire UK.
     One of the largest databases of crop circles can be found at the Internet site of:
     http://cropcircleconnector.com/2000/2000.html.

6.   Dr Richard Boylan. Here is an extract of his bio from his home page at:
     http://www.jps.net/drboylan/rjbbio.htm

     Dr. Richard J. Boylan is a Ph.D., behavioral scientist, university lecturer, certified clinical hypnotherapist, consultant, and researcher. He provides hypnotherapy for health improvement, reduction of stress and pain, habit change, and for exploring past personal events and life. Dr. Boylan is a consultant to persons exploring extraterrestrial encounters and other anomalous experiences, and assists individuals seeking inner growth and spiritual development.

7.   2001- A space Odyssey, 1968, Written by Arthur C. Clarke, and produced by Stanley Kubrick

8.   FURTHER DISCLOSURES BY CONSULTANT TO NATIONAL SECURITY COUNCIL'S SPECIAL [UFO/ET] STUDIES GROUP, DR. MICHAEL WOLF
     http://www.jps.net/drboylan/wlflk1.htm 1999

     Michael Wolf, MD, Ph.D., ScD, JD, is scientific consultant to the National Security Council's Special Studies Group (popularly known as MJ-12). In December, he began a new series of disclosures to the author. These are not "leaks", but are sanctioned by the U.S. Government under its "Processed Release of Information".

Commenting on the U.S. Government's Processed Release of Inforamation program, Dr. Wolf stated that the "Powers That Be [reactionary global control elite] resist disclosures, and want the pace of any information release tobe glacially slow. They fear that if extraterrestrial technology gets out into the public domain, (such as petroleum-coal-natural gas-uranium-replacing Zero-Point Energy, as well as pharmaceutical industry-replacing ET curatives for almost all diseases), that the elite's near-monopoly on wealth and power will be broken. Indeed, Wolf said that the government has operational cold fusion "in the back room." "We have modules that will restore [polluted] sea water to its natural state, as well as devices which connect to condensers and storage devices that produce unlimited energy." But, so fearful are those superwealthy power-brokers of ET technology replacing their crude and polluting assets, that a considerable amount of Black Project funds for the Project MILSTAR grid of DSP-1 UFO-surveillance satellites come from Oil States. [2] Dr. Wolf angrily retorted to the elite's selfish fears, "We need to cut through the crap!"....

...The UN maintains an unacknowledged Special Intelligence Branch, which is involved in working with all countries and their intelligence services around extraterrestrial matters. Dr. Wolf revealed that he is negotiating with an official within the UN's Security Council staff to have the UN release UFO information it possesses in 1999. This official has advanced degrees, and has been given "incredible powers" during her ET encounters. He says, "The UN people know everything (about the visiting ETS). And (Apollo astronauts) Edgar Mitchell and Gordon Cooper have made appeals to the UN to let the truth be known."

Author's Update

It is with regret that we reecently discovered that Dr. Michael Wolf passed away on September 16, 2000, after a long battle with cancer. We offer our cojndolences to his family and wish to recognizee his work in the field of promoting truth into the public domain.

We would also like to include this short eulogy by Dr. Robert Boylan concerning the passing of Dr. Michael Wolf:

He will be sorely missed. Dr. Wolf courageously struggled for the truth, and stood up to those who would keep the public in the dark forever about extraterrestrial presence.

His passing deprives us of his wisdom and warmth in life. Yet his spirit is now freed to do its work "from the other side", as he told me he planned to do after "crossing over". Thus he does not so much die, as in transition to a higher place, where he can continue to do spirit's work.

Hail! friend, scientist, soldier, patriot, lightworker!

—— Dr. Richard Boylan

Chapter 3

The Year 2012

The Relationship of Khufu and The Ark

Deep beneath the Gaza plateau is the "Ark of the Convent," or, more precisely, "The "! In an attempt to decipher the Giza Plateau and its important relationship to an understanding of our origins and society today, we will analyze the data that enables us to locate the position of the tombs of Osiris, Elnil and Joseph, under the plateau.

We believed that analysis of Giza-Genesis connection required, in part, a return to what the Ancient Egyptians termed "Zep Tepi," "The First Time." This is a time that spanned from the primeval oceans (Nun) to Horus and the redemption of Osiris, god of the underworld and resurrection. It is the period the ancients referred to as the "Time of the Gods," recorded in the heavens above. This was visualized and reflected in the display of the celestial orbs and constellations where the main "players" were such "gods" as Ra, (our sun), Osiris (Orion), Isis (Sirius) and Thoth (the moon).

We also mentioned that Genesis is the most complex, interwoven coded piece of literature ever written. We concluded there were three levels of work, the third level of which is the revealing of man's genetic code. In addition, we concluded that whoever wrote the book of Genesis had a) constructed the pyramid complex at Giza, and/or b) possessed intimate knowledge of the blueprint from which the complex was constructed.

In addition, we presented the thesis that the earth was conceived by two sets of lineage. The first was our solar sun, and the second is the mathematical set of the six identified in the Bible as Adam, Seth, Enosh, , Mahalalel, and Jared. Adam is our point of origin in our "star map" — zero degrees. For example,

Adam the star referred to as Alcyone in the Pleiades, Abram our sun, and Abraham our planet Earth.

This is only one example, however, since Genesis was written to reflect the same on many levels. It was written in this manner so as not to give a specific name to any particular object per se. However, it was utilized to point out lineage relationships.

When names are changed, that is, Adam to Abram, then Abram to Abraham, this is merely pointing out the different relationships toward which the text is directing the reader. An example of this would be Adam, as our sun, and due to the change in function, Abram is born (the planet Earth).

When the alignment of the planet Earth was realized, Abram then became known as Abraham. This was the alignment of the planet Earth falling under the influential force of the alignments of the stars from Orion and Sirius. Earth then became "Isaac," at which point it was at its second location, presently occupied by the planet Venus. Later it became "Jacob" or "Israel," when it reached its present position within the Solar system. When Earth reaches its next position, presently occupied by Mars, it will be known as "Joseph." However, it has yet to reach that location. Consequently, we are now entering into the time of Joseph. In other words, the names change only to clarify the relationship of the placement being discussed.

It is at this point that we offer an explanation towards an understanding of our origins and what is about to occur with the precursory event on .

GENESIS 5, VERSES 1 – 32

The first star in our set is Adam, from which it is important to remember that we establish the origin of all direction – i.e., the "Garden of Eden." Everything, including stars and planets east of that point of origin, has very distinctive reference co-ordinates, i.e., North, South, East and West. North is then established as "0" degrees, and thus we place Adam at this point. A complete cycle in our mathematics is 360 degrees. Thus, when Adam was 130 years old he had a son named Seth. Subsequently, he "lived" an additional 800 years, for a total of 930 years. What is important here are the figures 130 and 930. To triangulate the co-ordinates from Adam to Seth we must transpose Adam's life span into degrees.

We divide 360 into 930 to get the equivalent of one degree, resulting in 2.58333. Next, we multiply by 130, to establish Seth's alignment with Adam, for a total angle of 335.83332 degrees. We have now established the angle where Seth is relative to Adam.

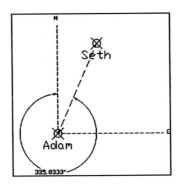

Figure 3.1 — Adam—Seth Lineage Chart

Our second alignment is from Seth, where we re-establish our "0" degrees North. The key numbers here are 105 and 912. Again we divide 912 by 360 degrees to get the equivalent of one degree, resulting in 2.533333. Next we multiply by 105 and arrive at a total of 265.9999 degrees.

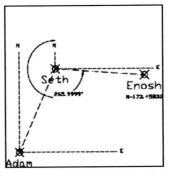

Figure 3.2 — Seth-Enoch Line

We have now established the angle where Enosh is relative to Seth. Our third alignment is from Enosh where the key numbers are 90 and 905. Again, we divide 905 by 360 to get the equivalent of one degree, resulting in 2.5138888. Next we multiply by 90 to establish 's alignment from Enosh, to a total of 226.24999 degrees. We now have established the angle where is relative to Enosh.

Our fourth alignment is from . From we re-establish our by 360, to acquire the equivalent of one degree, resulting in 2.527777. Next we multiply by 70 to establish 's alignment from Mahalelel for a total of 176.944443 degrees. We have now established the angle where Mahalelel is relative to .

Our fifth alignment is from Mahalelel. From Mahalelel we re-establish our "0" degrees North where the key numbers here are 65 and 895. Again we divide 895 by 360, to acquire the equivalent of one degree, resulting in 2,486111. Next we multiply 65 to establish Mahalelel's alignment from Jared for a total of 161.59722 degrees. We have now established the angle where Jared is relative to Mahalelel. From Jared our key numbers are 162 and 962. Again dividing 962 by 360, we establish one to be equal to 2.672222 degrees.

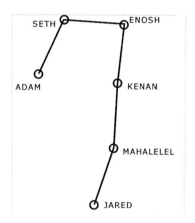

Figure 3.3 — Mahalel Line

Now multiplying 2.672222 by 162, we find this to be 432.89999. At Jared the normal sequencing appears to break down. Interestingly, however, that is not the case. Instead, we concluded that any numbers in excess of 360 indicated that we were to return to our original "0" degree-point and subtract 360 from our multiplication.

Therefore, we subtract 360 degrees from 432.89999 degrees and arrive at 72.89999 degrees. This becomes a set within a set, and we now return to our original "0" degree, which is Adam. We then extend a line outward from Adam at an angle of 72.89999 degrees using our original "0" degrees as being north, moving in an eastern direction.

This line represents Enoch.

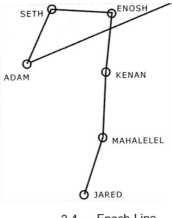

3.4 — Enoch Line

From Enoch, the significant numbers are 65 and 365. Once again, we divide 365 by 360 and find that one degree equals 1.01388. We then multiply 1.01388 by 65 resulting in 65.90277 degrees. Since this number is less than 360 degrees, this must be an angle that is calculated off the Enoch line. We arbitrarily picked a point on the Enoch line and measured inwardly, using East as our "0" degree point, 65.90277 degrees. This was our first indication that we are now dealing with three-dimensional form. We then draw a line out from Enoch and this now becomes the Methuselah line.

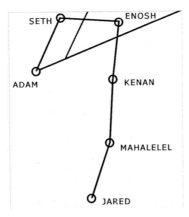

Figure 3.5—Methuselah Line

From Methuselah the significant numbers are 187 and 969. We divide 969 by 360 and find one degree to equal 2.69166. Continuing this process, we then multiplied 2.69166 by 187 and arrived at 503.34165 degrees. We now subtract 360 degrees to result in 143.34165 degrees. Having exceeded 360 degrees, we started back from the point called Adam. Again, dealing with three dimensional form, and previously used north as "0" degrees, we chose west this time, thus allowing the line to intersect or pass through the Methuselah line. Finally we extended our line out from Adam and labelled it .

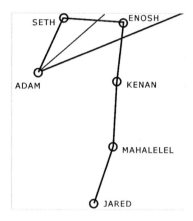

Figure 3.6 —— Lamech Line

From the numbers are 182 and 777. Again, we divide 777 by 360 and find one degree to equal 2.15833 degrees. Continuing through our process, we multiplied 2.15833 by182 and arrived at 392.81666 degrees.

This figure again exceeded our 360-degree model by 32.81666 degrees and again returned to Adam. Using our three dimensional form we used east as our "0" point and headed in a northerly direction and drew our line out from Adam at 32.81666 degrees to intersect or pass through the Methuselah line.

We call this line .

Figure 3.7
Noah Line Chart

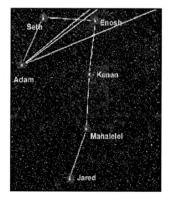

At this point we came to the conclusion that this was only half the working model. It has been established that the Pyramid of Khufu, by both its placement and precise interpretation of its measurements, is a scale model of the earth's Northern Hemisphere. We concluded that the second half of our model had to be precise. Therefore, we built a wire frame model using the Auto-CAD® software program; incorporating Piazzi Smyth's interior and Cole's exterior measurements.

We now placed our pyramid model of Khufu inside our Genesis model by aligning our pyramid's outer casing (south side) with the Enoch line and the center of the pit found in the subterranean chamber with the line. We then shot light beams down the two shafts into the and rotated our model until the northern shaft intersected exactly with the spot marked Adam. Consequently, the southern shaft lined up exactly with Seth, thus reinforcing our theory that both shafts are aimed at a downward direction, since they do not exit the pyramid. Next, the angle that our pyramid model intersects our Enoch line is slightly greater than 65.90277 degrees, or the point where our Methuselah line should have intersected with Enoch.

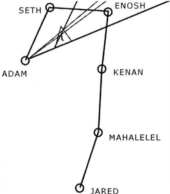

Figure 3.8 Line —— Intersecting to Queens' Chamber

Using a new meridian line on our pyramid model, we discovered that at this precise location, aligns with the entry to the passageway to the (our old meridian line is dead center) — therefore establishing a "0" degree alignment.

Unlike those found in the , both shafts in the exit the pyramid. The same will hold true (no exit) for the two proposed shafts that extend from the Grand Gallery. None of these shafts was ever intended to provide ventilation for the pyramid. Remember, the entire pyramid was once completely sealed by casing stones.

The two shafts from the and the two from the Grand Gallery all miss their target points. We measured the deviation in degrees in which the four shafts missed their respective target. The exact point where these two beams intersect is precisely the location of the hidden room and our new meridian line.

The discovery by Rudolph Gatenbrink[1] provided us with evidence that the angle changes approximately 80 feet up the northern shaft where there appears to be a turn. Also, the angle changes approximately 200 feet up the southern shaft where a door was discovered.

From these 200 and 80 foot points, we then projected a beam downward through our new meridian. While pivoting as well as re-scaling our model, it was initially noticed that all six shafts aligned with the star set, except those found in the . Also, the Lamach line intersected our new meridian line. The line intersected the Grand Gallery walkway precisely where we had previously established the beginning of the undiscovered passageway. The angle of degrees where the pyramid base intersects the Enoch line is 65.90277, the same angle given to us in Genesis, as the Methuselah line.

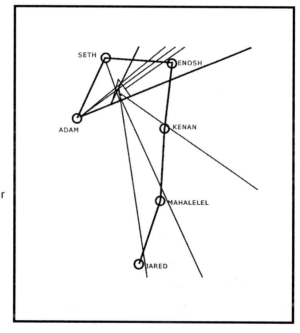

Figure 3.9
Meridian Point
of
Hidden Chamber

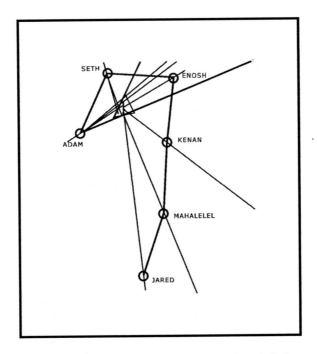

Figure 3.10 — Line and Intersection of Grand Gallery

Having now completed our interpretation of this Adam-Seth model and its relationship to the pyramid of Khufu, we conclude that's Ark, referred to in the Bible, may in fact be Khufu.

This essential and most sought-after information is the ultimate goal of many researchers and agencies, which have been attempting to gain access and therefore control for some time.

The entry to this "hidden passageway," which ultimately leads to the location of the "Covenant," can be found via the Grand Gallery within the Great Pyramid of Khufu. This is one of three entrances from which the may be accessed.

The following information will be the most important set of data released so far. We will furnish the evidence and information required, in order to activate the mechanism from within the Grand Gallery of the Great Pyramid of Khufu, and thus provide access to the hidden chamber. This in turn will lead to the covenant, or , whereby the advancement (to stabilize the earth's core, thus provide a "shield" around our atmosphere) is an essential and integral part of earth's protection and subsequent ascension.

Prior to our divulging this information, it is imperative for the reader to comprehend the Giza complex as a whole – that is, the relation of the Great Pyramid, the Ark of the Covenant and the separate location of the so-called Hall of Records (HOR).

In order to unravel the mystery behind the Plateau complex, first we had to identify the key elements present on the plateau. Once these were identified (11 pyramids, 4 Valley temples, 3 mortuary temples, 3 processionways, a Sphinx, as well as several boat pits) we knew we had the pieces with which to work.

The second half of the information we collected concerned the numbers and angles, which are very exact (as the pyramid of Cheops attests) and which we could observe. The numbers that were repeatedly encountered are:

30, 26.285°, 3.714, 15, 15°51'14". 3.

After successfully breaking the mathematical code in Genesis, and after having interpreted the interior of Cheops, we knew the information we had obtained related more to Cosmology. (Keep in mind that, as Peter Tompkins points out in our CD, *Probing the Great Pyramid*, the pyramid known as Cheops proves to be Earth-commensurate.) We felt that the elements that make up the complex at Giza were laid out so that, once interpreted, they would accurately reflect Earth's relationship to the Cosmos. It was on this premise that we began our interpretation, which, in the shortened, highlighted form, is presented in this chapter.

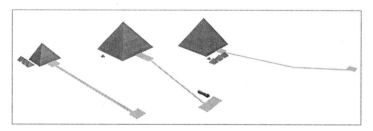

Figure 3.11 — Pyramid Plateau Layout

Place to one side for one moment, the pyramids of Menkaure, Khafre and Khufu (Cheops). Like all else connected to this complex, the real picture is revealed by unravelling the anomalies, whether apparent or becoming apparent in their absence. We established the outside perimeter as the Valley Temple of Khufu. The anomaly here was the 30° West-to-South-West angle which the processionway exits from the southwest corner of the temple. We then extended this angle past the point where the walkway makes a 15° turn to the west, and this line took us to the apex of the pyramid, which we now call Isis (the temple of Isis is located directly beside this pyramid on its east side).

Extending this line upwards, we found that it terminates at the northwest corner of Khafre's satellite pyramid (which has been dismantled for some time now). Descending to Khufu's Valley Temple, we drew a parallel line up from the southeast corner of the temple at a precise 30° angle, and found that this ended at the southwest corner of Khefre's satellite pyramid.

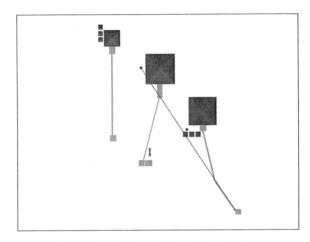

Figure 3.12 — Plateau Model No. 1

We then simply mirrored these lines complete with a replica of Khufu's Valley Temple attached, and connected Khufu's Valley Temple with the phantom temple. What we observed was a striking resemblance to the side view of the Khufu pyramid, as it sits on its base, even with the capstone missing. Further investigation revealed our pyramid model was exactly proportionate to Khufu with its base attached.

The pyramid Isis then became our focal point. (Remember, the symbol of Isis is a pyramid with an eye set in on its upper portion). From the center northwest corner of Khufu's Valley temple, we found that the apex of Khufu's satellite pyramid was also exactly 30° West-South-West.

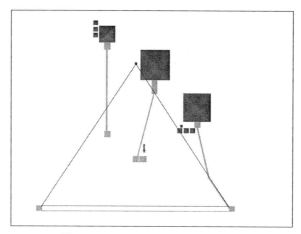

Figure 3.13—Plateau Model No. 2

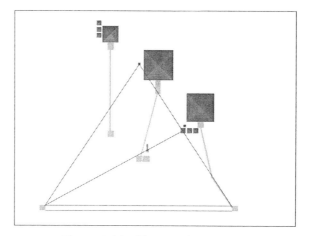

Figure 3.14—Plateau Model No. 3

A line leading from the apex of Khufu's satellite pyramid, directly across the apex of Isis, intersects dead center on the mid-point of their baselines. After completing measure alignments, we ended up with what appeared to be the profile of a pyramid that casts a shadow equal to the shadow cast at the time of the Winter Solstice, December 21. Also, looking down from atop Isis, our imaginary line crosses the right paw of the Sphinx. Could this indicate the point of entry into the legendary Hall of Records, spoken of by Edgar Cayce (See Chapter 13) or does it signal the location of our phantom temple? Theoretically, the phantom temple, according to our model, which is in relation to Isis, could be viewed as also being situated below the right paw of the Sphinx.

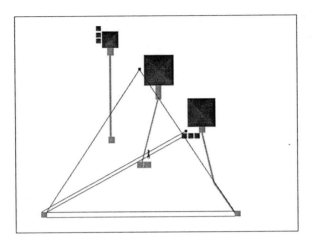

Figure 3.15—Plateau Model No. 4

Initially we believed that this could be the location, but additional information remained to be deciphered and verified. From this point, we will proceed only with the highlights.

1. (a) The three Queens' pyramids aligning North-South lying east of Khufu represent in this instance (remember that names change according to their function and point of context of reference) the planets (E) Earth, (V) Venus and (M) Mercury.

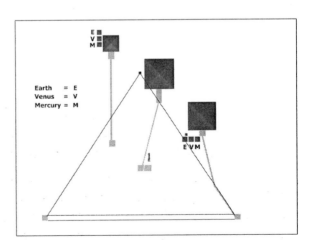

Figure 3.16
Earth—Venus—Mercury
Model
Layout No.1

(b) The three pyramids aligned East-West standing on the south side of Menkaura:

E = The angle from the center of the Earth to Alnitac on December 21st 2012

V = The angle from the center of Venus to Alnitac on December 21st 2012

M= The angle from the center of Mercury to Alnitac on December 21st 2012

Here is an example of how to read these:

Isis-Alnitac: From Isis, using due South as a 0° baseline, measure in degrees the angle, apex to apex. In this case the angle is 51°51'14", the precise angle of inclination of the Cheops pyramid. This angle represents the precise altitude at which Alnitac will be viewed from the apex of Isis (on a specific date).

2. Khafre's satellite pyramid's base was equal in length to the distance between the two entrances to the interior of Khafre's Valley temple. These align precisely to the center of the baseline of our overall model. We then moved the temple down, and along with it, the processionway. We attached mortuary temple until the outer edge of the wall of the temple (outer doorways) came to rest on the bottom baseline.

3. The Valley Temple of Menkaure with its processionway and mortuary temple attached was placed over Khafre's Valley Temple.

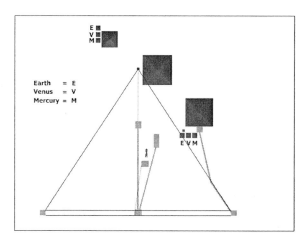

Figure 3.17 — Earth—Venus—Mercury Model Layout No. 2

4. The plan of Khufu's Valley Temple was initially slid up the processionway until it reached the point where the processionway angle changed by 15°. From this point forward, we then moved the temple, along with the remaining length of the processionway and mortuary temple, and placed it as well, atop Khafre's Valley temple.

5. (a) There is an angled separation lying between Khafre's Valley temple and the Sphinx temple. This angle is set at precisely 3.714°. When the Sphinx temple was slid down at this angle until its center point aligned with the apex of Khafre's satellite pyramid, we found it sits directly over the new placement of Khafre's Valley temple.

(b) When the Sphinx Valley temple is slid down to its proper placement, you .also bring the Sphinx with it, always keeping its spatial relationship to the temple intact. When all of the temples, including the Sphinx, have been re-located, the space below where these temples would rest is the precise location of the Hall of Records. This location has evaded detection by ground-sensing radar probing due to the fact that the town has been allowed to encroach onto the plateau site. Also, ground radar technology did not exist prior to the encroachments.

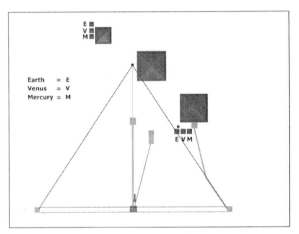

Figure 3.18 — Earth-Venus—Mercury Model Layout No. 3

The exact longitude and latitude is as follows, based on the accuracy of maps obtained from the map office in Cairo:

        Hall: Latitude   29°58'29"
              Longtitude   31°08'28"

The entrance into the Hall of Records is found directly between the paws of the Sphinx in its new location, and the surface entrance to the Hall of Records is found at the back end of the right paw of the Sphinx – in other words, in its new "theoretical" position. These locations are as accurate as you can obtain by using a G.P.S. locator.

The date of alignment as laid out on the plateau occurs on December 21, 2012 at almost precisely 2200 hours, 18 minutes, and approximately 13 seconds. Alignment is set at 150° minus 3.714° azimuth. This is as viewed from Isis and time is local Cairo time.

- Dec. 21, 2012 - Mayan long-count calendar ends.
- The adjustments to all 12 astrological houses will occur on that date.

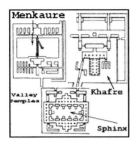

Figure 3.19
Temple Valley Floor
Plans

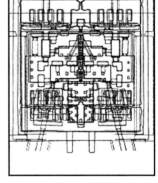

Figure 3.20
Overlay of Temple Floor Plans

Figure 3.21—Bob Lazar's Flying
Saucer &
Annihilation Reactor Chamber

Above is an overlay of all 3 of the Valley Temple floor plans, and a model drawing of Robert Lazar's flying saucer annihilation reactor system. We are not pursuing this data; however, our overlay certainly appears to present an electrically driven machine with circular moving parts, coupled with some sort of reaction chamber. Other than to point this out, we have nothing further to say on the matter.

The following illustrations are: (a) a picture of the opening leading into the Cheops pyramid, (b) a very detailed drawing (small section of his 30" x 36" drawing) drawn by Morton Edgar in 1909, above which we have shown a sized (and very accurately proportioned) Sphinx. (c) When we placed the Sphinx profile over the entrance (side view) we noted two factors: (1) the paws extend out to where the casing stone would have existed; (2) the rock anomaly, that shows up directly beneath the right paw of the Sphinx (note the angle).

The Hall of Records itself is very much represented inside the Cheops pyramid by way of the subterranean pit. If one were in the pit, one would then exit the room into a short level passage. At the end of that short passage, one would then look up a very steep passageway (the descending passageway). This would then lead out into the open spaces. The same will be found to be so when viewed from inside the Hall of Records. Keep in mind that the entrance to Cheops is offset from true North by 24 feet or 3.7142°. The Sphinx in its new location (to its center between the paws) will be 3.7142°.

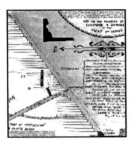
Figure 3.22
Opening of Cheop's Pyramid No.1

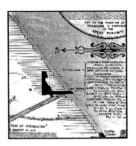
Figure 3.23
Opening of Cheop's Pyramid No. 2

This is the inside view looking out; therefore, the entrance appears on the right side of center in our model (rather than the usual view, from the outside of Cheops, which places the entrance on the left side of center). The entrance to the HOR can be seen to have been established under the south paw of the Sphinx, but only when the Sphinx has been moved down to its calculated position, i.e., after moving the entire associated valley temples, etc., to their aligned position.

This location was given as:

Latitude   29 deg. 58' 29"
Longitude   31 deg. 08' 28"

As we follow this important evidence, it may prove useful to bear in mind the following information. The present location of the Sphinx is exactly 15 degrees, when calculated from the west end of the right paw, up to the midpoint of the bottom casing stone located on the east side of the Great Pyramid. From that very point, it is precisely 30 degrees in elevation to the center point of the sarcophagus (the "Coffer") located in the . This enables us to point out that from the Hall of Records we can establish the precise location of the tomb of

Osiris! Indeed, the sarcophagus of Osiris and the sarcophagus of the are the same! Remember the adage of the Hermetic texts, "As above, so below." In this case it is, "As it is inside, so is it outside."

This same principle may be applied to the location for the second tomb, as marked out in the case of Khafre. The location of this tomb is calculated from the data, which represents the corner angle of the entrance to the Great Pyramid. Thus, the location of the first and third "Queens' " pyramids adjacent to the Great Pyramid.

We will analyze more of these pyramids in the following chapters.

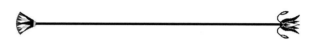

Notes

1   Rudolph Gatenbrink, German engineer and pioneer of the "Upuaut Project" where a small   robotic device was devised in order to analyze the small shafts of the pyramid of Khufu.

Chapter 4

The Covenant, or the Crystal

Having now established the location of the Hall of Records, we are now imparting to you the knowledge of the separate location of the 'Covenant'. We consider this to be one of the most important pieces of knowledge divulged so far, and rightly should be shared with those interested and concerned with the future of this planet and all that dwell upon it. The hidden chamber, as we will explain in detail, is accessed through an opening in the Grand Gallery, from where an access point, under a thin rock located in the floor of the room, will ultimately lead to the 'covenant'. This chamber, where the 'Covenant' can be found, is formed by a natural cavity within the limestone below the Great Pyramid.

On the eastside of the Great Pyramid are located three smaller 'satellite' pyramids, known as the 'Queen's pyramids', so named as they were believed to be associated with the wives of the Pharaoh Khufu. The middle pyramid of these three lies on the line that precedes the chamber of the Covenant, which in fact is located under the adjacent southern pyramid known as Horus, or Isis. It is this room that is accessed from within the hidden chamber via the Grand Gallery. The passageway leading from this hidden chamber to the inner room is shown inside the Great Pyramid by the presence of the WELL, both in its method of entry as well as its exit. That is, the doorway leading out to the horizontal subterranean chamber. All of these 'measurements' and markings are incorporated into the Great Pyramid's overall design.

Bearing this revelation in mind, we continue...

DECIPHERING THE INTERIOR OF THE GREAT PYRAMID

Entrance to the hidden passageway must be exact, but on the other hand must be constructed so as to avoid accidental detection. Therefore, the construction of this mechanism to access the inner sanctum must be made to ensure any attempt at entry would be a major undertaking, a co-ordinated team effort.

A "key" or code of great complexity would have to exist in order to gain access to this subterranean site. Thus the following information has been deciphered, understood and mathematically applied, so as to give the location leading to the hidden passageway and in turn access to the "covenant" or crystal.

THE PHYSICAL EVIDENCE

To comprehend as to what this is all about in our search for the hidden chambers and thus to the stored 'covenant' under the Giza plateau, we must begin by identifying and deciphering the intricacies involved in the layout of the Giza Plateau once more.

We commence at the point on the baseline due east of the satellite (Queen's) pyramid of the Great pyramid, termed as Horus, coincidentally between which can be found the Temple of Isis. From this point on the baseline, a line is drawn directly to the intersecting point, where the procession way (of Khufu) abruptly changes direction by 15 degrees and then heads on up to Khufu's mortuary temple. This angle is found to be precisely 50 degrees (Using our baseline as 0 degrees). Interestingly enough we find that a line drawn out in the opposite direction (using the baseline as 0 degrees reference point) at 51.42857 degrees not only crosses over the right paw of the sphinx but it crosses over the exact point we previously described as the entrance point to the Hall of Records (once the Sphinx is re-located to it's proper location).

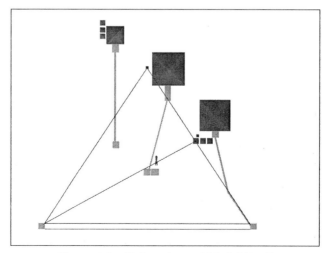

Figure 4.1 - Plateau Layout Model No. 5

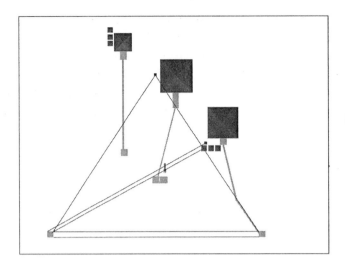

Figure 4.2 - Plateau
Layout Model
No. 6

The above figures of 50 and 51.42857 degrees are highly significant figures as we will soon see, while the other notable angle is the 15 degrees shift in the procession way. It is this 15-degree angle we will now explain.

Remember, the original angle as it left Khufu's' Valley Temple from the South-west corner was originally 30 degrees as it heads out directed towards the pyramid of 'Horus', the 15-degree correction we find is now culminating to the centre of the Great Pyramid. The original angle of 30 degrees being split exactly in half resulting in being directed at the centre of the east side of the G.P. We then start back at the Valley Temple and begin to extend a line out from the centre point of the West wall at exactly 15 degrees to find that the end point intersects with the N.E. corner of the G.P. "Shades of Mirror Imaging." To be exact it lines up precisely to the centre point of the corner casing stone.

Once that single point was identified, the entire complex then opened up completely for decipherment, doing so in the following manner.

Figure 4.3
Great Pyramid Diagram,
Showing Layers

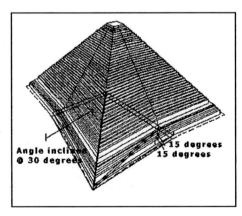

You can recall that the angle in degrees that we pointed out was precisely 50 degrees of arc from the center of the outside casing stone base up along the side of the existing Great Pyramid. It was further noted that from the outer outside edge of the same casing stone, the angle would have been precisely 51.4285 degrees to the apex, only if one factored in the casing stone. (It is worthy to note that from the point we measured and found the 50-degree incline, there is a very precise 10 degree arc spread between our 50-degree angle and the angle of the incline on the outside edge of the casing stone.)

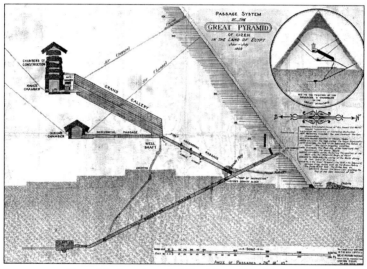

Figure 4.4 - Inner Layout of Great Pyramid by Morton

Next, taking the small pyramid up from the bottom baseline, incline it inward placing the mid point on the centre of the casing stone measuring point. It is then sized so that it's end points align to the centres of the north and east face of the Great Pyramid. Bear in mind the small pyramid that was brought up was extended out along the original baseline and terminated in the exact spot of the much larger pyramid (And was also used to locate the H.O.R.) Further evidence demonstrating that this had to be constructed in this manner is the shadow of the small black pyramid, which gave us the date of Dec 21st, is showing the sun sets in the West, not in the North. By moving the side of the small black pyramid to the east face of the Great Pyramid the shadow would then fall in an Easterly direction.

Finally, let us examine the north side.

The Valley Temple side of the small black pyramid demonstrates that entry is made in the centre of an above ground structure or temple. The remaining elements on the plateau we will explain when we disclose the events and the physics which drive them as they will occur on Dec 21, 2012.

In the following chapter we will demonstrate how to locate the entrance to the hidden chamber. As with the plateau complex overall, one simply had to compute and read the layout and distinguishing features. We will also explain how to activate the opening mechanism. We list below the important elements that demonstrate the calculations arrived at, after which an explanation as to how this all fits together will be described in detail.

1. First, prior to entry one is aware that the entrance is offset 24 feet or 1.42857 degrees from due north.

2. The angle of the Descending passageway is 26.28571 degrees which should be 30 degrees (30-3.714285=26.28571)

3. The angle of ascending passageway is 26.28571 degrees, which should be 30 degrees (30-3.714285=26.28571) 3.7142857= arc spread of zero when 3 zeros intersect at 30 degree angles. Thus 1.42857= Value of zero

4. The Passageway leading to the Queen's Chamber from entry point of passage to the point where step down occurs and drops down to floor level, is equal to 1.42857 degrees of arc.

5. From the corner when one first enters the Grand Galley and on the same level as the passageway leading to Queen's Chamber 30 degrees of arc, is the height of the top of the parallel ledges that run up the Grand Gallery.

6. From the outside edge of the Great Pyramid's casing stone at a level equal to the floor in the Queen's Chamber it is exactly 30 degrees of arc to the top of the roof of the King's Chamber.

7. The five (5) tiered niche inside Queen's Chamber begins at floor level, while the top of the peak of the King's 5 level ceiling has an arc between the 2 of 30 degrees thus the connection to the two.

8. The top tip of the roof over Queen's Chamber is offset from the centre of the hole in the floor of the Subterranean Chamber by 3.714285 degrees of Vertical arc.

9. The two stacked up, inlaid peaked rocks found above the entrance to the pyramid, point to the following. The peak of the lower one is exactly equal to the height of the floor level of the passageway leading to the Queen's Chamber. The upper one is exactly equal to the maximum height of the walkway in Grand Gallery where the passageway to Queen's Chamber begins, the point where the abrupt wall starts.

10. The angle correction to the existing ascending passage, measured from the point where the ascending and descending passage intersect to an exact 30 degrees, intersects the Grand Gallery walkway at the precise level as the base of the 34th tier of the Great Pyramid. The 35th tier is equal to the floor level height below the 20th mortise.

Chapter 5

The Book of Exodus

Before proceeding to an explanation of how one can open the hidden passageway via the Grand Gallery, it is important to understand the basic methods of construction, materials utilized, and location and reasoning behind the builders' selection.

The book of Genesis was based on theoretical physics with hard testable data. Exodus, however, is more of a philosophical text; it tells "the who, where, how and why." Exodus 25 and 26 deal with the dwelling (sanctuary) and furnishings (materials) that when placed together, form the sanctuary: ". . .They will make a sanctuary for me that I will dwell in their midst. This dwelling and all its furnishings you shall make exactly according to the pattern that I will now show you." (Exodus. 25:8-9)

The information is encoded in three parts in the text: the description of the material, the numbers used, and the method. All three parts together deliver the whole.

The key to understanding the passage can be found solely by one's ability to correctly decipher the various materials used in the construction – for example, acacia wood. Acacia is a tree or shrub from which gum Arabic is obtained. The term is applied to a flexible or pliable material, giving way to pressure. Gold is a mineral that is also soft and pliable (sandstone and granite are minerals) so whenever the term "gold" is applied, they are referring to rock. Whenever a specific number is used as a measurement or reference to a quantitative total, it refers to units. Units are not to be confused with measurements, since nowhere in the text do they ever establish any fixed measurements. However, units are referred to as independent visual anomalies. Therefore, it is concluded that the numbers used are real.

PLAN OF THE ARK

Based on the premise that Noah's Ark is a structure rather than a "boat," we will assume that Noah's Ark is in fact part of the Great Pyramid. It is therefore proposed that the Ark, in which the covenant (crystal) is stored, be accessed from the room inside the Great Pyramid known as the Grand Gallery. When opened, it will lead to the chamber where the Covenant is located.

> Exodus 25:10
>
> *You shall make an ark of Acacia wood, two and a half cubits long, one and a half cubits wide, one and a half cubits high.*
>
> *The two main visible elements here are the two ledges and center walkway. The ledges are equivalent to two units.*

Figure 5.1 — The Grand Gallery No. 1

> Exodus 25:11-Rock structure and gold plating:
>
> *Plate it inside and outside with pure gold and put a molding of gold around the top of it.*

This passage states that the entire structure is made from gold, or rock. The moldings referred to are the walls of the gallery.

Exodus 25:12

> *Cast four gold rings and fasten them on the four supports of the Ark, two rings on one side and two on the opposite end.*

This refers to the drilling of four holes into the rock, which is directly adjacent to the ends of the two ledges.

Exodus 25:13:

> *Then make poles of acacia wood and plate them with gold.*

The construction of the two ledges is of solid rock in order to make them somewhat flexible. The pins are then placed in each end of either ledge and in turn placed into the drilled four holes. One pin is placed in each corner, with the weight of the ledges carried by the pins; although more importantly, to hold the ledges in place.

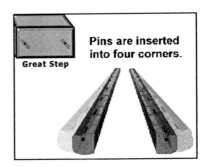

Figure 5.2

The Four Pins

Pins are inserted into four corners.

Great Step

Exodus 25:14-15

> *These poles you are to put through the rings on the sides of the ark for carrying it. The poles shall remain in the rings of the ark; they shall not be taken from it.*

It is imperative that these pins never be removed.

Exodus 13:16

> *In the ark you are to put the commandments which I will give you.*

This point is where the contents must be placed into the ark. The next steps are those taken to seal the ark.

Exodus 25:17 - Sealing of the Ark
> *You shall then make a propitiatory of pure gold, two cubits and*
> *a half long, and one and a half cubits wide*

Here, the instructions are given to cover up the ark or seal it completely with rock.

Exodus 25:18
> *Make two cherubim of beaten gold for the two ends of the*
> *propitiatory.*

At each end of the gallery the walls are cut out so as to have winged sides.

Exodus 25:19
> *Fasten them so that one cherub springs direct from each end*

Between the two ends are placed winged rocks, which run continuously from end to end. This refers to the corbelled ceiling rocks, which appear winged-like.

Exodus 25:20 - The Seven Corbels
> *The cherubim shall have their wings spread out above, covering*
> *the propitiatory with them; they shall be turned toward each other,*
> *but with their faces looking toward the propitiatory.*

Once again, the seven-corbelled ceiling faces inward as it looks down on the cover that sits over the ark.

Exodus 25:21
> *This propitiatory you shall then place on top of the ark. In the*
> *Ark you are to put the commandments which I will give you.*

Again, referring to the corbelled ceiling that sits above the ark.

Exodus 25:22 - Indication of Size of the Object.
> *There I shall meet you and there from above the propitiatory*
> *be the two cherubim on the ark of the commandments I will tell you*
> *all the commands that I wish to give the Israelites*

This is a clear indication that what we are dealing with is not a small object carried by one or two persons, as we have traditionally been led to believe.

Figure 5.3 —— The Grand Gallery No. 2

Exodus 25:23 - The Ledges and the Table.

You shall also make a table of acacia wood, two cubits long, a cubit wide and a cubit and a half high.

This refers to a combined length, which includes the ledges, one unit; and the walkway, the second unit. The width is equivalent to one unit (walkway and ledges combined). The height, as we have previously established, is the opening that leads to the Queen's chamber and location of a second opening that exists but remains covered. The second location, because it is covered, is therefore only represented as half a unit.

Exodus 25:24 - Solid Rock Material

Place it with pure gold and make a molding of gold around it.

Once again the material to be used is solid rock. The earlier reference of acacia wood indicates to us that in some fashion it is pliable. The moldings referred to here are the two ledges.

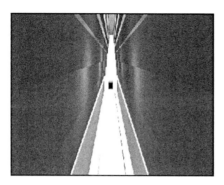

Figure 5.4 —— The Ledges and Tables

Exodus 25:25 - The Side Walls of the Gallery
Surround it with a frame, a handbreadth high, with a molding of gold around the frame.

The frame represents the sidewalls of the gallery. The "handbreadth high" means that if one stood on the ledge and extended one's arms up to where the bottom of the first corbel begins, it measures approximately three inches.

Figure 5.5 —— The Grand Gallery No. 3

Exodus 25:26-27 - The Four Holes and Iron Pins
[pins placed connecting each ledge]
You shall make four rings of gold for it and fasten them at the four corners, one at each leg on two opposite sides of the frame as holders for the poles to carry the table. The four rings are the four holes that were drilled in the two end walls, where the iron pins are fixed to the ledge that carries the table

Exodus 25:28
These poles for carrying the table you shall make of acacia wood and plate with gold.

These ledges are made of solid rock; the use of the term 'acacia wood' indicates the ledges have some sort of moveable function.

Exodus 25:29
Of pure gold you shall make its plates and cups, as well as its pitchers and bowls for poring libations.

The cups sit on the plate or mantel, which refer to the mortises. These mortises are cut into the top, flat part, of the ledges. The cups are equally spaced on each ledge. The bowls refer to the holes cut out along the inside wall of the lower part of these ledges, from which, when tilted, something is released.

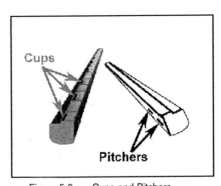

Figure 5.6 —— Cups and Pitchers

Exodus 25:30 - Showbread: Entrance to the Passageway
On the table you shall always keep show-bread set before me.

The "showbread" is the entrance leading to the Queen's chamber, with its leveled-out entrance. Both sit out in front of the "table." This entrance has been left open to expose the clue of the point of entry leading to the Queen's chamber, the passageway or walkway that had to be lowered.

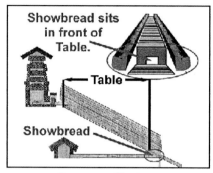

Figure 5.7—Showbread

Exodus 25:31 - The Lamp-Stand, or the Two End Walls
You shall make a lamp stand of pure beaten gold, with shaft and branches with its cups and knobs and petals springing directly from it.

The term "lamp stand" refers to the two end walls of the Grand gallery, which are cut out of rock, and when separated, allow one to see all of which comprises the area within the space itself. The knobs are the molded levels upon which the corbels sit, and from which they extend.

Exodus 25:32-33
On one branch, there are to be three cups, shaped like almond blossoms, each with its knob and petals; on the opposite branch there are to be three cups, shaped like almond blossoms, each with its knob and petals; and so for the six branches that extend from the lamp stand.

The three branches are the corbelled ceiling, the sidewall and finally the ledge. The three cups represent the holes that are cut into each ledge and the sidewall. The first is the mortises; the second, the hole cut into the wall vertically above each mortise; the third is the hole cut horizontally into the sidewall.

Figure 5.8—Grand Gallery No. 4 Showing the Lampstands

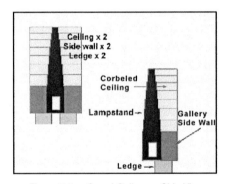

Figure 5.9—Grand Gallery—Side View

All three placements of these cut-out sections occur directly opposite from each other.

Exodus 25:34-35

> *On the shaft there are to be four cups shaped like almond blossoms, with their knobs and petals, including a knob below each of the three pairs of branches that extend from the lamp stand.*

This section states that in addition to the already established three holes, there is a further hole cut into the ledge. These holes, or knobs, are carved from the sidewalls on each ledge.

Exodus 25:36 - The Ledges are Cemented Together
Their knobs and branches shall so spring from it that the whole will form but a single piece of pure beaten gold.

It is pointed out here that the ledges are cemented together, so as to form a single unit, on either side of the walkway of the Grand Gallery.

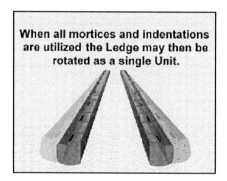

Figure 5.10—The Cemented Ledges

Exodus 25:37 - The Seven Girdle Stones
You shall make seven lamps for it and so set the lamps that they shed their light on the space in front of the lamp stand.

This refers to the placement of the seven girdle-type stones that are being held in place between the two ledges, that is, the seven rocks (sheets), each with a hole (light) cut out. When in place, the holes align, forming a passage facing the "lamp stand."

Figure 5.11
The Seven Girdle Stones

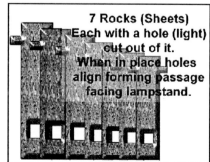

Exodus 25:38

These, as well as the trimming shears and trays, must be of
pure gold.

Again, stating that these girdle stones are made of solid rock, as are the
pieces that are sitting on top of the grand gallery, which are connecting both
sets of corbels. These other pieces are made of moveable, square-cut rock,
which have been used to complete the roof of the Grand Gallery.

Exodus 25:39-40

Use a talent of pure gold for the lamp stand and all its utensils.
See that you make them according to the pattern shown you
on the mountain.

We are reminded of the large amount of rock required to complete the
room itself, which was built to a very specific pattern, literally a mountain of
stone! Also, the large wall at each end of the room is fashioned so as to be
able to support the weight of the side corbels.

Exodus 26:1

The dwelling itself you shall make out of the sheets woven of fine
linen twined and of violet, purple and scarlet yarn, with cherubim
embroidered on them.

Now we begin to deal with all the parts. Here are instructions for assembling
the mechanism which, when actuated, forms the passageway leading to the hidden
room. The moving pieces are made of red granite and have wing-like pieces or
protrusions extending from both sides.

Figure 5.12
The Various Sections and Parts

Exodus 26:2

The length of each shall be 28 cubits and the width four cubits;
all the sheets shall be of the same size.

The length of 28 units refer to the four guides that are cut into the side walls, that direct the seven sheets down into their proper place, once they are released. These four guides are comprised of two sets of two; the first set runs the entire length of the rock (sheets). The second set runs down only a short way, guiding the upper arm that extrudes from the side of each sheet. The width of the four units is the two above-mentioned sets of guides, which appear on either side of each sheet.

Exodus 26:3

Five of the sheets to be sewed together, edge-to-edge and the
same for the other five.

This indicates that there are five pieces glued together to form a single unit. One such unit is the piece that lies in front of the entrance to the passageway leading to the Queen's Chamber. The second piece has yet to be dropped into place. This will expose the entrance to the passageway leading to the hidden room.

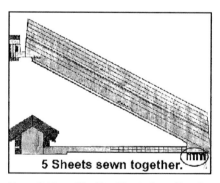

Figure 5.13 —— The Five Sheets Sewn Together

Exodus 26:4

Make loops of violet yarn along the edge of the end sheet in
one set, and the same along the edge of the end sheet in
the other set

These are the wing-like protrusions at the side of those girdle stones; each set has an equal number of these winged protrusions.

Exodus 26:5

> *There are to be 50 loops along the edge of the end sheet in the first set, and 50 loops along the edge of the corresponding sheet in the second set and so placed that the loops are directly opposite each other.*

This section refers to the top 50 mortises in the grand gallery, 25 on each side, and the 50 holes which are centered directly below each mortise, on the inside of each ledge and cut into the ledge wall below the walkway height.

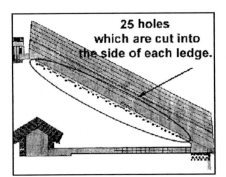 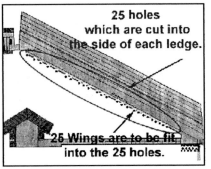

Figures 5.14 & 5.15 —— The 25 Holes on Each Side, & Wings Fitted into the 25 Holes

Exodus 26:6

> *Then make 50 clasps of gold, with which to join the two sets of sheets, so that the dwelling forms one whole.*

There are 50 winged protrusions that align with 50 holes, 25 on either side that fit into the corresponding holes so as to appear to be one unit.

Exodus 26:7-8-9

> *Also make sheets woven of goat hair to be used as a tent covering over the dwelling. Eleven such sheets are to be made; the length of each shall be 30 cubits, and the width four cubits. All eleven sheets shall be of the same size. Sew five of the sheets, edge to edge, into one set, and the other six sheets into another set. Use the sixth sheet double at the front of the tent.*

At this point we are dealing with two distinct units. The first unit is made of five sheets, which are dropped in front of the Queen's Chamber passageway. The second unit is made of six sheets, which will drop when the mechanism is activated, thus exposing the entrance of the hidden room passageway.

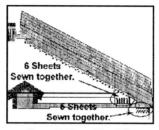

Figure 5.16 —— The Units

The length of 30 units is equivalent to the 25 holes carved into the sidewall of each ledge, plus the added five units already exposed at the entrance of the Grand Gallery.

The width of the four units refers to the cavities cut into the side of each ledge as well as the wing-like rock that fits into these cavities.

Exodus 26:10

Make 50 loops along the edge of the end sheet in one set, and 50 loops along the edge of the end sheet in the second set.

The 50 units referred to here, sit on top of part of the ledge; 25 are the mortises atop each ledge. The other 25 are those carved into the wall immediately adjacent This is duplicated on the opposite ledge.

Exodus 26:11

Also make 50-bronzed clasps and put them into the loops, to join the tent into one hole.

The bronze clasps refer to the hard-ridged, wooden posts. These posts are fitted into the mortises and extend the full height of the vertical section of the cross-shaped indentation, appearing directly above each mortise. This is the key element used to activate the mechanism. Once actuated, it will allow the passageway to form.

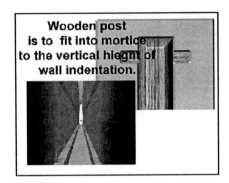

Figure 5.17
The Post and Mortice

Exodus 26:12-13

> *There will be an extra half-sheet of tent covering which shall be*
> *allowed to hang down over the rear of the dwelling. Likewise*
> *sheets of the tent will have an extra cubit length to be left hanging*
> *down on either side of the dwelling to protect it.*

The extra half-sheet at the rear, ending in front of the great step is equal to half the length between the two mortises. On the other end, this part extends past the Queen's chamber passage opening, and is centered under the 25th mortise.

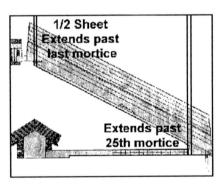

Figure 5.18 —— Mortice & Sheets

Exodus 26:14

> *Over the tent itself you shall make a covering of ram's skin,*
> *dyed red, and above that, a covering of tahash skins.*

The rock used under the walkway is composed of red granite. The top part, or the walkway itself, is made of the much softer sandstone.

Exodus 26:15-16

> *You shall make boards of acacia wood as walls for the dwell*
> *ing. The length of each board is to be ten cubits, and its width*
> *one and a half cubits.*

Once again, the use of acacia wood indicates that these are flexible rock and made to be moveable. The ten units referred to simply mean that there are ten such rocks. The width of one-and-a-half units spans the width of the walkway, and is affixed halfway into the ledges.

Exodus 26:17

> *Each board shall have two arms that shall serve to fasten the*
> *boards in line. In this way all the boards of the dwelling are to*
> *be made.*

The arms mentioned here are the wing-like ends, which protrude from the side of each moving rock. These wings are used to hold the sheets in place until released.

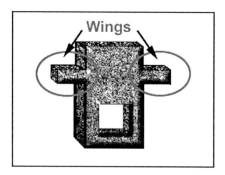

Figure 5.19—The Wings

Exodus 26:18-19

> *Set up the boards of the dwelling as follows: 20 boards on the*
> *south side, with 40 silver pedestals under the 20 boards, so that*
> *there are two pedestals under each board at its two arms.*

The 20 boards are guides on either side of the ten falling rocks. The guides are used to direct and control the moving rock. The same holds true for each arm, which are the shorter pedestals located only at the top end of the rock. Similar guides are visible in the sidewalls of the portcullis, or antechamber.

Exodus 26:20-21

> *Twenty boards on the other side of the dwelling, the North*
> *side, with their 40 silver pedestals, two under each board.*

The same applies as explained above, except they are using the north side. Furthermore, they are referring to the sheets, or rocks, and their respective pedestals, which are formed from their guides.

Exodus 26:22

> *Six boards for the rear of the dwelling to the west.*

These six moveable rocks are those cemented together to form the unit referred to as the veil.

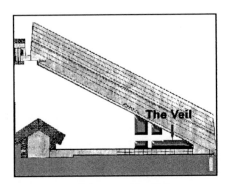

Figure 5.20 —— The Veil

Exodus 26:23-24

> *And two boards for the corners at the rear of the dwelling to the*
> *west. These two shall be double at the bottom and likewise*
> *double at the top, to the first ring. That is how both boards*
> *in the corners are to be made.*

Again, this refers to the doubling-up of the rocks at either end of the ledges, into which the iron pins are placed.

Exodus 26:25

> *Thus, there shall be in the rear eight boards, with their 16*
> *silver pedestals, two pedestals under each board.*

Each board is generally equated to one sheet, when we have included the ends; we have to remember each is doubled up. Again, there are two guides cut into the rock, positioning each board, or rock, into place.

Exodus 26:26-27
Also make bars of acacia wood: five for the boards on one side, and five for those at the rear, toward the West.

These refer to the boards that comprise the veil, one that has been released, and the other waiting to be released. This is made apparent by the direct reference of using both sides. Only one side is mentioned here, that being the west side; however, the opposite equally exists (that is the east side). Boards are used to describe the square holes that are put into the stone.

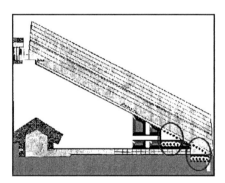

Figure 5.21—The Boards and Veil

Exodus 26:28-29
The center bar, at the middle of the boards, shall reach across from end to end. Plate the boards with gold, and make gold rings on them as holders for the bars, which are also to be plated.

The passageway is the square hole cut into the center part of each board. When all boards are aligned, these girdle-type stones, with the square holes running through them, form the passageway.

Exodus 26:30
You shall erect the dwelling according to the pattern shown you on the mountain.

The pattern shown is found to be the present position of the veil located in front of the Queen's passageway entrance.

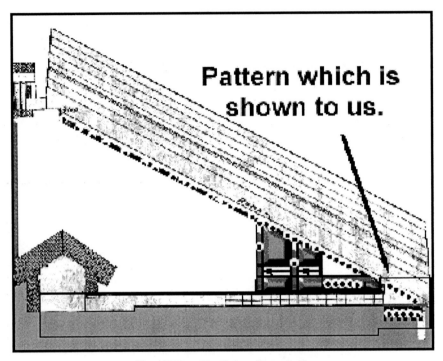

Figure 5.22 ——The Pattern Shown to Us

Exodus 26:31,32
> *You shall have a veil woven of violet, purple and scarlet yarn,*
> *and a fine linen, with cherubim embroidered on it. It is to be,*
> *on four gold-plated columns of acacia wood, which shall have*
> *hooks of gold and rest on four silver pedestals.*

Already described was how the veil was constructed, and where it is situated. The four rock columns are the two ledges that held up the two veils. The two ledges are held with iron bars.

Exodus 26:33-34
> *Hang the veil from clasps. The ark of the commandments*
> *you shall bring inside, behind this veil, which divides the*
> *holy place from the holy of holies.Set the propitiatory on*
> *the ark of the commandments in the holy of holies.*

The veil is held in place by the arms or wings, which protrude from it. The veil separates the sanctuary, the Grand Gallery, from the holy of holies that lies within.

Exodus 26:35

> *Outside the veil you shall place the table and the lamp stand, the latter on the south side of the dwelling, opposite the table, which is to be put on the north side.*

The opening of the new passageway faces directly to the south end wall of the gallery. This wall is the lamp stand. Running north above this entrance is the still intact table or walkway and ledges.

Figure 5.23 —— The Table and Lampstand

Exodus 26:36-37

> *For the entrance of the tent make a variegated curtain of violet, purple and scarlet yarn and of fine linen twined. Make five columns of acacia wood for this curtain: have them plated with gold, with their hooks of gold, and cast five bronze pedestals for them.*

Finally, the veil is the entrance to the "tent" which, when accessed, leads to the place where the covenant is kept. The veil is held in place by the extended arms of the sheet of rocks. Closed, it sits in place with its arms locked into the adjacent notches in the ledge walls. To expose this entrance, we must release the arms from the notches.

Additional Note:

After reading the evidence that we have placed before you, it may worth considering the following section from:

Exodus 25:22:

> *There I will meet you and there from above the propitiatory, between the two cherubim on the ark of the commandments, I will tell you all the commands that I wish you to give the Israelites.*

In the Grand Gallery are located 50 mortises, 25 on either side, and into each of these a wedge is positioned, located between the post and adjacent wall. Each wedge is driven downward, causing a pivoting effect, thus pushing the bottom of the ledges outward while simultaneously causing the top to lean inward.

The east and west ledge stones, lying on either side of the gallery, are cemented together so as to move the whole as one stone. Under these ledges is a layer of sand, deposited for a definitive ultimate purpose. Later, we will discuss the recent discovery of this sand, especially in the Queen's Chamber, and its purpose.

METHOD OF OPERATING MECHANISM

A continuous downward pressure from each of these wedges causes a rock at the lower end of each wedge to be forced out and subsequently fall. As these rocks fall, so does the layer of sand, thus creating a shifting surface below the ledges. This surface allows the walkways to rotate slightly, and it is during this process that the two ledges separate further.

This structure is composed of 11 rocks, but not all of these rocks will actually move. A few of them along the top of the center walkway will fall to expose the entrance to the passageway. The remaining rocks above and below this level will remain in place on the walkway. However, it seems that there are at least seven other rocks located beneath the walkway level, shaped, in part, like a girdle stone.

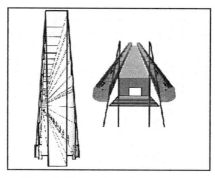

Figure 5.24 - The Operating Mechanism

These girdle stones are made of a harder granite rock, and when released, will slide along guides that will direct their fall. Eventually they will land on a bed of sand, softening the impact and thus prevent shattering.

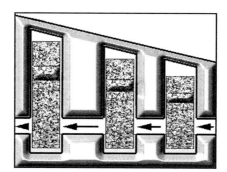

Figure 5.25—The Girdle Stones

The main purpose of the granite rocks is to prevent accidental exposure of the opening itself, thus lessening the probability that a solid straight open cavity, or passageway, could be detected. These granite stones have small wing-like protrusions extending out from the sides, to hold the stones in place when the two ledges of the gallery are in the closed position. This was done by cutting cavities into the adjacent locations in the ledges themselves.

Initially, the ledges were built with their moveable rocks in place. In order to accomplish this, the outside ledges were locked in an open position. When each rock was added to the ledge and cemented together, it was imperative that, as construction progresses, the ledges be left open.

The rocks themselves were held open by inserting posts up along the wall, adjacent to the ledges; finally wedging them into place. To ensure that the walkway could be closed, it was necessary to incorporate a method to release and remove these wedges and posts. This was realized by carving a crosshaped indentation above each mortise. Once the walkway reached the height to which the Great Step was to be placed, a hole was drilled into both ledges and an iron pin inserted. Corresponding holes were then drilled into the Great Step, which was then fitted to connect with the ledges. The great step now became part of the hinge mechanism.

Once the mechanism was in place, sand was poured in, allowing the massive weight of the ledges to rest upon the sand, until such time when the opening would be activated. When the ledges were all in place, they were driven down into the horizontal section carved into the walls of the gallery above each mortise. These vertical sections of the carvings provide the required height and width of the posts for operating at maximum efficiency. Upon the wedges being driven down into these vertical slots, the posts and wedges could then be ignored, and the capping stones of the center walkway could finally be positioned into place.

By using the anomalies present (the various types of stone) in the passageway leading to the Queen's Chamber, the total length of the hidden passageway can be calculated. Upon entering the passageway, the type of stone changes to a much harder rock. Farther along the passage, it takes an abrupt drop of two feet. Thus a significant factor is the total length from where this harder rock begins, until the drop-off point.

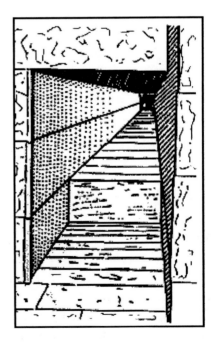

Running horizontally, we find it to be equal to the length required for our new passageway to commence, carrying through to the point where our proposed point of intersection occurs. The second clue is that in order to enter the existing Queen's Chamber, one must step down. This indicates that the passageway we are seeking must exist above this level.

Both ledges, which flank the opening, have five recesses cut into them directly opposite each other.

Figure 5.26 — The Step

These are all cut below the level of the walkway, which runs up the gallery; thus providing evidence that the method of entry was present by the existence of these recesses that once held the center walkway. Once the mechanism is activated, this will allow the five sheets, sewn together, to be released, and thus fall. These sheets are referred to as the veil.

Figure 5.27—North End of Gallery

If they had been free-falling, the floor would have been anything less than smooth.

The next stage was the removal of the end of one of the side ledges, thus exposing the . It was near this entrance that the first iron pin was discovered. Farther down the well, at the "Grotto," a granite block is located with a hole drilled into it. This block was left to give the impression it had fallen down the from the entry point of the well inside the Grand Gallery.

The provided an area for the sand to exit into, thus allowing for easier pivoting of both side ledges. Also, it is important to note that an additional pin was discovered embedded into the wall down toward the bottom of the .

Additional evidence is incorporated in the Great Gallery. First, the moveable rocks located on the roof of the Gallery are not cemented together, and the ceiling width is close to being the width of the center walkway running up the Gallery. This allowed for the marking of the fifth corbel, which was previously established to be the fifth shaft, while also enabling the determination of the location of the sixth shaft and its point of intersection.

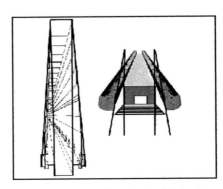

Figure 5.28 ——The Great Gallery Mechanism

In addition, it reinforced the premise that when we lever out the two ledges on either side of the walkway, this would cause them to flare outward at their base. This effect seems to have been caused as if the relative angle of the corbel ceiling had been wedged from above the ceiling itself. Thus driving down a one-inch wedge at the top would easily move the bottom of the rock out 3-4 inches.

Chapter 6

The Great Step

It is feasible that this rock structure could have been built with two or more stones. However, to maintain the distance and angle of the two side ledges, one massive stone was used and pinned to both ledges, ensuring that no movement occurred.

Figure 6.1—The Step

If indeed shifting did occur, the moveable rocks may have been misaligned, in turn creating a number of problems.

In the ascending passageway are two important elements. First are the granite plugs, constructed and placed so as to be moveable. Each of these plugs was originally placed behind the second important feature of this passage, the three girdle stones. If these three girdle stones were not in position, three blockages would have been found behind the granite plugs. By their very presence they create an obstructed passageway.

Circe AD 820, when Caliph Al Ma'mun, a 9th century Muslim governor and his men chiselled their way into the Great pyramid, they must have dislodged small wedges that held back the girdle stone. The resonant shock waves caused by their hammering must have knocked these stones loose, thus allowing the three granite plugs to slide freely downward until making contact with the granite block. (Hence, the noise reported from within.)

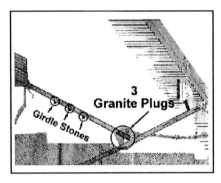

Figure 6.2—The Three Granite Plugs

The force of impact when the plugs came into contact with the granite block and thin limestone block, which concealed the entrance to the ascending passageway, forced them both into the descending passageway.

It is the girdle stone apparatus, which when released by the wedging of the two side ledges, will fall into place and complete the formation of the hidden passageway.

Finally, located at the other end of the great gallery is the "Portcullis" or antechamber. Here, all the rock is composed of red granite. This room is interpreted as follows: The slabs of red granite are guided into their desired positions, thus creating a passageway located on a horizontal line.

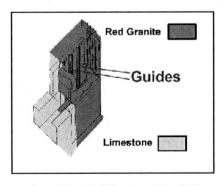

Figure 6.3—Red Granite and the Girdles

We have now discussed in detail the majority of the elements required to justify the proposed mechanism. However, one or two points remain. One is the pivoted door, believed to have been incorporated as the entrance to the Great Pyramid. This would have required two pins on which the door could pivot

In 1987, two French architects, Gilles Dormion and Jean Patrice Godin, were undergoing excavation work in the Great Pyramid, where they drilled a few holes in and around the area of the Queen's Chamber. From one of the holes they drilled in the passageway leading to the Queen's Chamber, sand began to pour out, plugging the hole. At the time, no reason was known as to why this sand was there. However, we suggest that the sand was incorporated for a specific purpose, i.e., for the girdle stones to land upon, once released; thus, softening the landing.

THE RELATIONSHIP BETWEEN NOAH'S ARK AND THE GRAND GALLERY

Genesis indicates that the Ark is 50 cubits in width and there are 50 mortises in the gallery, 25 on either side. The passage below seems to tell us what this is about:

They shall make a sanctuary for me, that I may dwell in their midst.
This dwelling and all its furnishings you shall make exactly according to the pattern that I will now show you.

EXODUS 25: 8-9

The Book of Exodus reveals the pattern of the Ark into which the covenant (The Crystal) was to be stored, and the decoding of the relevant passages demonstrates that the Ark is in fact built and contained in its entirety in an area specifically referred to as the Grand Gallery.

Having briefly described the physical evidence above, we now offer an explanation as to the actual "physics" involved. This will give us a possible understanding of the complex set of geometrical configuration involved.

It is advisable to follow this explanation in association with the main illustration of the layout of the interior of the Great Pyramid. Where appropriate, we have included additional illustrations in order to enhance the reader's understanding.

To prove our thesis, the initial task is to establish the location of the two chambers — that is, the King's and Queen's chambers.

We begin by establishing the end points that are to be utilized as the constants; thus:

1. The very bottom of the outside casing stone found directly below the entrance way to the descending passageway.
2. The midpoint of the above-mentioned casing stone to its inside, also calculated from the base level.
3. The Apex of the roof of the Queen's Chamber (upper outside edge).
4. The Apex of the roof of the King's Chamber (the upper outside edge of the Apex found above the fifth tier).

First, we will measure the elevation to the Apex of the Queen's Chamber from the outside edge of the casing stone. (All measurements used in the following 4 angles of elevation will utilize the base platform on which the casing stone rests, as 0 degrees elevation). From the outside edge of the casing stone, we find that the degrees in elevation is a very precise 15 degrees, 0 minutes and 0 seconds.

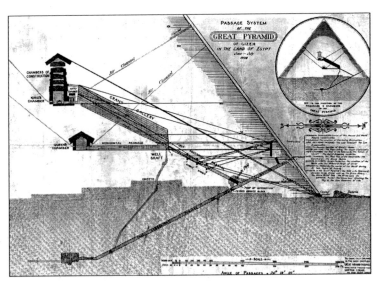

Figure 6.4—Great Pyramid Internal Layout No. 1

It is also extremely important to note that the 15-degree angle intersects the front edge of the third girdle stone located in the ascending passage at the precise point where the girdle stone meets the passageway floor.

The next measurement is also taken from the outside edge of the outer casing stone and extends upward to the Apex point of the King's Chamber roof. This angle of elevation is exactly 30 degrees 0 minutes 0 seconds. It is vital to note that this line crosses very precisely where the "scored line" intersects with the ceiling of the descending passageway.

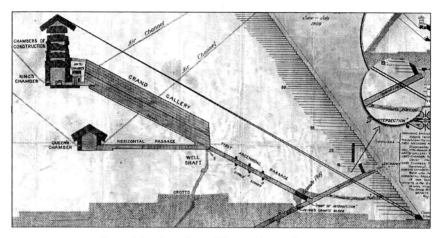

Figure 6.5—Great Pyramid Internal Layout No. 2

The next two angles are taken from the center point of the outside casing stone where it rests on the platform. Once again, the platform is utilized as being our 0-degree point. The angle is then calculated, as previously used, to the Apex of the Queen's Chamber roof. We find this angle to equal 13.57143 degrees, thus calculating the measurement once again of 1.42857 degrees (15-13.57143=1.42857). It is also important to note that the projected angle of 13.57143 degrees crosses at the exact point where the third girdle stone (located in the ascending passageway) outside edge intersects with the passageway ceiling.

The second stage is to calculate the angle of the elevation to the Apex of the King's Chamber from the center point of the outside casing stone. It is concluded that this angle is a very precise 28.57143 degrees. (Once again we find 30-28.57143=1.42857 degrees of deviation.) We also note that this projected angle intersects at the precise spot where the "scored line" intersects with the floor in the descending passageway.

To understand the placement of the entranceway to Khufu's pyramid, we must utilize the information we previously disclosed as interpreted from the whole Giza complex markings. Once we established the center point as being the outside edge of the bottom casing stone, located on the North East corner, we can then begin to understand the data which the layout of the interior of the Great Pyramid has to show us, thus:

A. The entranceway is offset from due North 1.42857 degrees.

B. From the cornerstone as measured from the outside edge of the casing stone between the northeast to the northwest cornerstones we find the mid-point of the center of the pyramid is offset 1.42857 degrees.

C. From the outside bottom of the northeast casing stone we find that the entrance point to the Great Pyramid is at a precise elevation of 15 degrees.

D. From the center point of the casing stone directly in line with the north east angle we find that the 15-degree elevation aligns to the face of the 30th tier rock, in direct line North-South, where the existing opening is located.

Before one enters the pyramid, and looking up, are two sets of angled rocks above the entrance. These are generally thought as having been placed so as to relieve the pressure of the weight of the mass of rock above the opening. From an engineering point of view, they may very well have. However, these have a much more complex and intricate purpose. We refer to the Apex of each set as the lower and upper marking tips.

Figure 6.6—The Great Pyramid Entrance

Below is a list, although not in its entirety, of the crucial data that helps to point out the following:

A. The lower marking Apex tip is at the precise elevation as the floor level in the Queen's Chamber.

B. The upper marking Apex tip is at the precise elevation as the height of the cut-off point of the passageway in the Grand Gallery, that is directly above the entrance to the passageway leading into the Queen's Chamber.

C. From the outside edge of the upper marking Apex point using a North South line as 0 degrees, we find that a 15-degree angle in a downward direction from the horizontal intersects where the upper inside corner of the middle girdle stone intersects with the ascending passageway floor.

D. The upper marking from the inside edge also shot at a downward 15-degree angle, intersects the point where the outside edge of the middle girdle stone intersects with the passageway floor.

E. The outside edge of the lower marking Apex point once again shooting down precisely 15 degrees — we find this line intersects with the upper side of the first girdle stone where it intersects with the roof of the ascending passageway.

F. From the inside edge of the lower marking apex we find that a 15-degree line intersects with the upper inside corner of the first girdle stone where it intersects the passageway.

G. From the outside edge of the lower marking we find that a 15-degree angle, in an upward direction, marks the precise point on the South Gallery wall where the top of the carved line (etched into the bottom section of the fifth corbel) intersects the wall.

H. From the inside edge of the lower marking we discover that also at 15 degrees upward, this is the location where the bottom section of the line intersects with the South Gallery wall.

I. From the upper marking outside apex measuring up 15 degrees (from the horizontal) we notice that this is precisely where the roof in the Grand Gallery intersects with the south wall of the Gallery.

J. From the inside edge of the upper marking, once again using our 15-degree elevated projecting, we find that this line intersects at the exact point where the bottom edge of the seventh corbel intersects the south Gallery wall.

Additional markings are pointed out, and are derived from these two markers; however, at this point in time it is not necessary to go into any detail.

Before continuing with our analysis, it is important to note that the "original entrance" aligns precisely with the opening created by the upper stone, the girdle stone, in the ascending passageway. The top of the original entrance is at the same elevation as the upper, outside edge of the girdle stone. The bottom of the original entrance doorway is at the same elevation as the bottom inside corner of the girdle stone, where it intersects the floor of the ascending passageway.

The next calculation is from the outside casing stone at the base of the pyramid, where we measure from the base at the center point of the casing stone up at a 15-degree angle once again. This angle, in elevation, is found to intersect the inside edge of the middle girdle stone where the ascending passageway floor meets. In addition, from this same location, we mark the point where the inside edge of the girdle stone intersects the passageway floor. This is found to be precisely 30 degrees, to the point where the top of the line carved into the bottom of the fifth corbel intersects the south wall in the Gallery. The outside edge intersects the base of the seventh corbel stone at the south wall.

We now measure from the floor where the middle girdle stone intersects the floor from both its inside and outside points; only this time, we measure in the opposite direction at precise angles (from each point) of 15 degrees. Initially, we find that from the inside of the girdle stone and floor level, this reaches out to the very upper outside edge of the 30th tier outer stone. At a 15-degree angle from the outside edge of the point where the girdle stone intersects with the passageway floor, this line ends precisely at the bottom outside edge of the outside rock on the 30th tier.

Numerous measurements can be calculated from the subterranean chamber and passageway located down beneath the Great Pyramid. However, in this section we will deal only with those required in establishing the location of the entranceway to the hidden room, which will eventually lead us to the final resting place of the "Ark of the Covenant."

The initial measurement is taken from the floor level on the south end of the recessed area in the passageway leading horizontally into the Subterranean Chamber. This point is used because it is directly below the old meridian of the pyramid. The old meridian ran up from this point, passing through the apex of the ceiling inside the Queen's Chamber, thus carrying on upward.

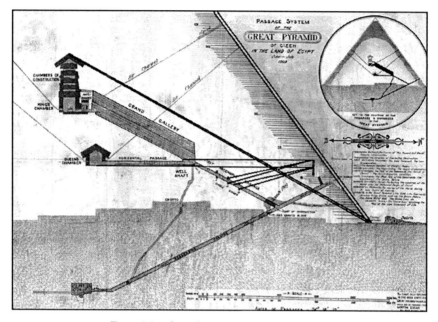

Figure 6.7——Great Pyramid - Internal Layout No. 3

From this location at floor level in the descending passageway, we calculate our angle northward 30 degrees. When this line is extended outward, it is found that it passes through the point where the roof of the passageway (leading into the Queen's Chamber) meetsthe Grand Gallery. We further note that this line extends upward and intersects the exact point where the Gallery ceiling meets the north wall of the Grand Gallery itself.

Next, we move to the inside of the subterranean Chamber, taking our 30-degree measurement angle once again from where the passageway meets the north wall of the subterranean chamber, measuring from floor level of the room. When we broke the mathematical code in Genesis, it offered the new meridian line that proved out to an accuracy of its seventh decimal point. Consequently, this is the reason for taking the measurement at this point.

We found that the new meridian line from this point upward passes through the Queen's Chamber on the very edge of the bottom level of the five-tiered niche on its south side. It then extends upward, running up the very backside of the Great Step, culminating at the point where the seventh corbel intersects the south wall of the Gallery.

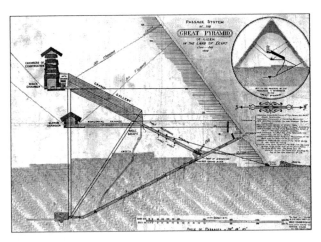

Figure 6.8——Great Pyramid - Internal Layout No. 4

When we extend this line up, we discover that it intersects the Grand Gallery walkway at the precise height of elevation where the base of the rock is on the 30th tier of the pyramid, when a horizontal line is extended inward from same.

Taking the subterranean measurements provides us with the tools to construct the calculations, as if we were taking them from 0 degrees elevation from the outside base near the center of the east face of the pyramid.

It is now found that at the base of the 25th tier of the pyramid, or the top of the 24th tier, is the exact elevation as the floor in the Queen's Chamber. Measuring from the top of the 24th tier puts us up 6 tiers (or sheets of rock) to the 30th tier. This would be equal to the number of sheets to the second veil as mentioned in Exodus. The first veil is equal to the number of courses from the entrance point on the 19th tier level to the passageway level on the 24th level (5 tiers), which is 5 sheets.

At the top of the Grand Gallery, the entrance level to the King's Chamber is at the same level as the top edge of the Great Step. This level, when extended outward in a northerly direction, is found to be precisely equal to the height of the 50th tier. The cut-off for the new passageway leading into the hidden room is located directly beneath the 20th mortise, counting down from the top, which is the exact height of the 35th tier of the Great Pyramid. This fact is one reason that the 35th tier is different in size, etc. In addition, it also supports further anomalies, such as: 1) The five-tiered niche in the Queens' Chamber, 2) The five-tiered ceiling in the King's chamber, and 3) The five corbels marked from the line on the bottom of the fifth corbel to the roof of the Grand Gallery.

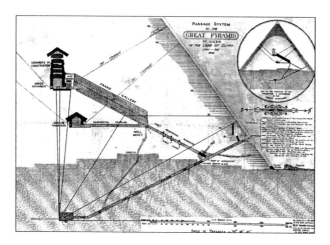

Figure 6.9——Great Pyramid - Internal Layout No. 5

PRECAUTIONARY ADVICE

Once the passageway is formed, at the far end it will be found to be blocked by a single rock. When pushed inward, it will reveal the existence of a new chamber. Prior to the moving of this rock into the room, we advise that certain precautions be taken.

Care must be taken so as to prevent the rush of air into this chamber. It is suggested that two vapor/air barriers be placed inside the passageway, thus alleviating the chances of contamination to material within. In addition, it is also believed that once access to the chamber is activated, there are only three days in which to reach the final designated location.

Two relatively recent discoveries in and around the Great Pyramid are of importance to those who will continue with the undertaking of reaching this hidden chamber. These are:

1. The discovery by Gatenbrink of the doorway, or the rock blocking the shaft that the Upuaut robot encountered in the shaft inside the Queen's Chamber.

2. The underground passageway, discovered by Joseph Schor[1] leading out from beneath the Great Pyramid to the three satellite, or "Queens' Pyramids," which continue beneath these pyramids.

The computer-generated model over a satellite photograph of the three main Giza pyramids show the location of the "coffer" in the King's chamber, indicating that there is something contained in the space beneath the "Queens' Pyramids." Again, what is above is mirrored below.

METHOD OF ACCESS TO HIDDEN CHAMBER

Upon entering the chamber, off to the right-hand side at floor level, a thin rock is located, which when lifted will expose the entrance to a new shaft. This in turn leads down and out into the hidden chamber.

The rock placement was made easier to determine its location, since it sits precisely at the angle that intersects the meridian from where Gatenbrink's thin rock is located. Indeed, this was the sole purpose for the placement of this rock blocking the shaft. Once this rock is lifted, one must proceed down and out into the chamber where the Covenant (Crystal) is stored. Extreme caution is advised.

It may be of interest to note that the "recently discovered tomb of Osiris"[2] is located approximately 100 feet below the causeway of the pyramid of Khafre. Below is a photograph of this "coffin." On close inspection, the "petrified remains" of the structure under the coffer cover in the background appear to be of a reptilian life form.

CONCLUSION

It is expected that by reading and analyzing the research offered above, the reader will come to realize the true nature of what we have been attempting to explain.

By examining one of the many ancient sites that are to be analyzed, we can see that there was a collective purpose, an integration or applied network of advanced knowledge that spanned the globe. This knowledge was collected so that one day it would be understood and utilized.

We feel that the time is now rapidly approaching when this "ancient" knowledge should be divulged, assimilated and utilized for its ultimate purpose.

What exactly is that purpose? To allow the earth and its inhabitants to realize the next phase in the development of growth. This phase is often referred to by some as "Ascension." Ascension will demonstrate our true origins in the cosmos, and it is necessary in order to "free" ourselves from the presently acceptable yet limited knowledge that has been fed to us over time.

Notes

1.   Schor, Dr. Joseph Schor, of the Schor Foundation New York. Schor is a long-standing member of the Association for Research and Enlightenment (A.R.E.), the organization founded by Edgar Cayce in 1931.

2.   This so called "tomb of Osiris" was allegedly opened "live" April 1999, and filmed as a "Fox TV Special". The "Osiris Shaft" is located under the causeway of Khafre, and it is about 25 feet deep. The shaft opens in the causeway linking the Sphinx to the second pyramid, and it descends in several places to a depth of nearly 100 feet below. It was here that four pillars were discovered where within was found part of a large granite sarcopha gus with its lid thrown off.

The complete story may be found at the homepage of Zahi Hawass (site director) at:
   http://guardians.net/hawass/osiris1.htm

Chapter 7

Door Number Two

EDGAR'S REVENGE

Before one can truly establish the location of the Three Tombs beneath the GIZA Plateau, one must demonstrate how to decipher the important measurements that are made from within the Subterranean Chamber located beneath the Great Pyramid of Khufu (Cheops). Combined with the internal alignments of the pyramid of Khufu, this subterranean chamber is one of the major pivotal components required to fully decipher the blueprint of the Plateau's external secrets.

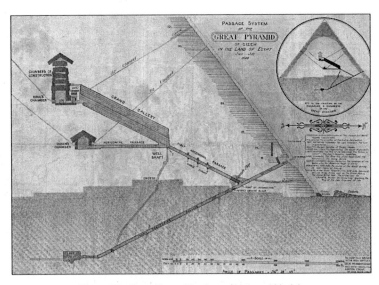

Figure 7.1 - Great Pyramid – General Internal Model

We will concentrate on the angle measurements from within the subterranean chambers in which they are directly related to the precise locations. These are, in fact, clearly marked in the pyramid itself. From within the chamber we will be using three precise reference points: the north wall of the chamber (where it intersects with the floor), the south wall of the chamber (where it intersects with the floor), and the center point of the Pit, located inside the chamber. All calculations are made from the level to which the Pit was originally cut.

SOUTH WALL

Using as our reference point the place where the south wall intersects with the floor, it is found this is located directly beneath the north outside face of the sarcophagus (the "Coffer") situated in the King's Chamber. Now, utilizing this place as the vertical reference point, or our zero (0) degree, we calculate the angle to the south outside face of the sarcophagus. This was found to be precisely 1.42857 degrees of arc from our original reference point. From this identical reference point we calculated a 30-degree arc line from our vertical zero degree line, and projected it up into the interior of the pyramid. This line was projected in a south to north direction.

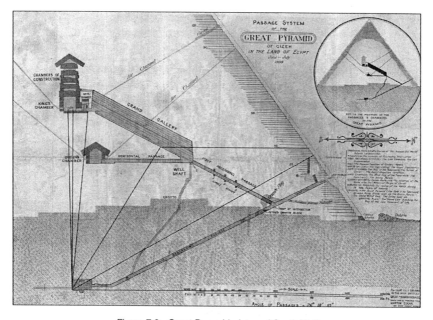

Figure 7.2 - Great Pyramid - Internal South Wall

It was discovered that this line intersected at the exact height of 1137.6 inches above the pyramid base, the horizontal line drawn in from the point where the 34th and 35th tiered stones meet. This point of intersection was and is, the same point on the ledge in the Grand Gallery that we had previously identified as the cut-off (drop) point of the Second Veil. Proceeding to use our south wall-floor reference point, we then projected a 30-degree arc up and outwards, to the exterior of the pyramid; however, on this occasion using the horizontal plane as our zero-degree reference line. This line was found to cross the very corner of the top of the outer stone located on the 30th tier. In addition, it was noted that this line crosses the inside edge of the upper marking stone located above the original entrance to the Descending Passageway.

The other measurement, taken from the south wall at floor level reference point, was taken using our vertical zero degree line, but this time in a northern arc projection of 5 degrees. This end point marks the location where the portcullis passageway begins at the end of the Grand Gallery.

Our second point of reference is located at floor level of the north wall of the subterranean chamber. Vertically, this wall aligns with the south wall of the Grand Gallery. From this vertical line at the reference point, a 30-degree angle was projected upward, where it intersects a horizontal line drawn in from the rock on the outside of the pyramid located on the 30th tier. Where these lines cross is the point in the Grand Gallery where the projected floor level, leading into the secret room, is believed to be located.

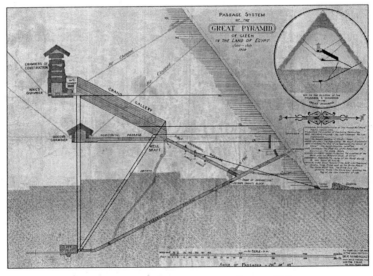

Figure 7.3 - Great Pyramid - Internal North Wall

Previously, we pointed out that where the recessed point was located outside the Subterranean Chamber, the vertical line intersected the front edge of the Great Step. The vertical line drawn up from the Subterranean Chamber's north wall also marks the point where the back end of the Great Step is located inside the Grand Gallery.

The third point of measurement from within the Subterranean Chamber is the pit itself. This is taken from its original center point. However, if a vertical line is drawn straight up from the south wall of the pit, this line marks the location of the north wall (inside face) in the King's Chamber. Drawing a vertical line up from the north wall of the pit actually marks the spot where the south end of the portcullis wall ends. From our main reference point, the center of the pit, once a vertical line is extended upward, it will be observed that this line dead ends precisely where the center of the rock (which was pushed into the King's Chamber) would have been originally placed.

Further, using this vertical line as the zero (0) degree point, and using our maximum 30-degree arc spread, we find that this projected line intersects at the top of the ledge located in the Grand Gallery. This also intersects with ahorizontal line drawn inward from the top of the stone located on the 35th tier. A second arc was drawn at a 15-degree angle from the center of the pit up from the vertical, and it was observed that this line marked the exact upper cut-off point where the passageway leading to the Queen's Chamber drops down.

The entrance into the secret room itself is located where the 30-degree arc, drawn up from the south wall vertical reference point, intersects with the extended vertical line drawn inward from the bottom of the stone on the 30th tier. The difference in length from this point of intersection, to the point where the Veil drops down, exposing the passageway, is the length required for *seven* slabs of stone along with the guide spacings. (This is based on the overall length of the four slabs with their guides included, shown to us by their presence in the Portcullis.)

The Book of Revelation Refers to These Seven Slabs as the Seven Seals.

In a previous chapter, we explained the exact location of the Hall of Records; it is from this location that all three major tombs can be accurately calculated as to their exact locations beneath the Plateau. However, prior to identifying the locations of the tombs themselves, we will demonstrate how the respective locations of the Subterranean Chamber and the Hall of Records provide the pivotal points for the required accuracy in order to make the necessary calculations.

From the phantom room, located on the south end point of our plateau model layout at its baseline and using the baseline itself as our zero-degree reference point, we make our first 30-degree arc measurement. This projected line crosses the apex of the pyramid of Horus (the southernmost "satellite" or Queen's Pyramid of Khufu) while continuing and completing when it intersects with a line which is drawn through the center of the Pyramid of Khufu (Cheops), in an east to west direction. This intersection actually occurs at the base casing stone located at the center of the east face of the Pyramid. The 30-degree line originated from the southeast corner of the room.

This process is then repeated, however, from the southwest corner of the room, and it is discovered that this line crosses over the apex where the satellite pyramidof Khufu sat previously.

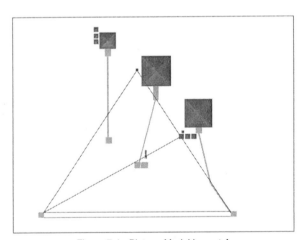

Figure 7.4 - Plateau Model Layout A

Extending this line further, it is found to reach the outside edge of the bottom casing stone located dead center on the north face of Khufu, noting that this is also on a North-South meridian. The point where the two meridian lines intersect is of course, when projected inward, in the Subterranean Chamber. Always remember that the external layout reflects the internal layout.

We will now proceedto demonstrate how the trhee pyramids , Khufu, Khafre and Menkaure, which lie outside our plateau pyramid model, are represented on the inside of the model- that is, with the exception of the southeast corner of Khafre, which is physically situated inside our model pyramid. Later we will deal with this indiscriminate variable.

At this point, we wish to demonstrate how and where these three pyramids are to be "theoretically" brought down and placed within the plateau model. Previously, we established the placement of the Pyramid of Khufu, which occurred when we were calculating the exact location of the Hall of Records. The perimeters of its placement are from the southwest corner of the Valley Temple of Khufu, upward at a 30-degree angle, to the apex of the pyramid of Horus, then back down to the baseline at a 30-degree angle from the vertical, which lies due east of the apex of Horus. This intersection point is the center

of our baseline and the centrsal point pof the Hall of Records. The resulting triangle formed as a rewsult of this represents the Pyramid of Khufu.

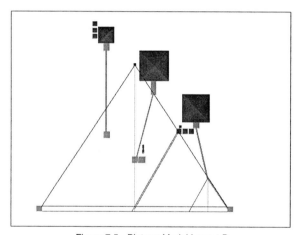

Figure 7.5 - Plateau Model Layout B

From the apex of the satellite Pyramid of Khufu, at the same 30-degree angle when extended down towards the Hall of Records, marks the southwest corner of the room itself. While drawn down in the opposite direction, it marks the northwest wall of Khufu's Valley Temple. Menkaure is brought into the plateau model in the following manner, while again, commencing in the southwest corner of the Valley Temple of Khufu and proceeding up at the same 30-degree angle line used to establish Khufu's placement within the model. However, we extend upward only as far as the place where the processionway alters its course 15 degrees, and continues on to Khufu's mortuary temple. The place where this processionway deviates from its point of origin, at the Valley Temple, and then swings sharply up 15 degrees, is cross-calculated using the following method:

Pivoting the whole complex precisely 120 degrees, using the apex of the Pyramid of Khufu as the pivot point, we find that the southeast corner of Khufu's Pyramid aligns precisely where the processionway alters its direction — that is to say, if we draw a line down from where the very corner of the rotated pyramid (southeast corner) would be positioned once rotated, and only if this line were to be drawn, or extended out from that precise point absolutely due East.

Using the point where the processionway alters course as the apex, we then calculate our 30-degree angle as previously when we were dealing with the apex of Horus. Once a line is extended down at the 30-degree angle, until it intersects the baseline, the triangle we have created represents the pyramid of Menkaure and thus its intended placement within the plateau model.

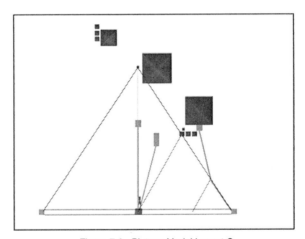

Figure 7.6 - Plateau Model Layout C

Khafre's Pyramid was more complex to bring down and place within the plateau model, so we returned to our blueprint model, the interior of Khufu. The most obvious measurement we had to work with was the 15-degree angle, which originates from the center of the pit in the Subterranean Chamber extending up to where the cut-off step in the passageway leading to the Queen's Chamber is located. Utilizing this angle makes perfect sense due to the fact that the processionway leading to Khafre's Mortuary Temple is also angled at 15 degrees. In addition, having shown why the Valley Temple of Khafre is brought down to the location of the Hall of Records, located at the baseline of the Plateau model, it was decided to use this same angle.

The problem now arose as to how to locate the entrance to this Tomb. We already concluded that the entrance to the tomb was slightly below the Primary Tomb, which is located beneath Horus. In order to locate the precise location we had to initially identify some other point of reference, which in fact proved to be easier than it first appeared.

The primary two angles used throughout, proved to be 15 or 30 degrees. A brief glimpse and two possible specifically marked reference points became obvious. These were identified as the points directly due East of the apexes of our two previously placed pyramids, that is, Menkaura and Khufu. From Khufu's baseline center point, we shot an angle upward to where it intersects with the 15-degree angle from the location of the Hall of Records. Then, from Menkaure's base center point, we used the 30-degree angle. It was not surprising to find that it intersected precisely where the two 15-degree lines intersected.

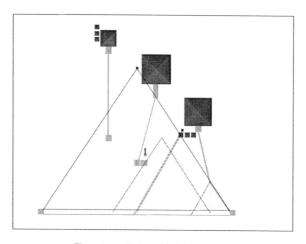

Figure 7.7 - Plateau Model Layout D

This point of intersection is where we fixed our apex. Next, we drew our usual 30-degree line down to the baseline so as to establish the south face of the pyramid, as we had previously carried out with the other two pyramids. However, at first glance it did not appear correct, since the 30-degree line intersected the Plateau model baseline well, on the other side of the Hall of Records. Obviously, that was the reason the southeast corner of the physical Khafren pyramid was extended into the plateau model, showing that it did in fact cross the line.

This also explains why the northwest corner of Horus was allowed to extend outside the plateau model, since its main entrance is only accessible from within Khufu.

Once the three pyramid silhouettes are in place, many points become obvious to the eye. First, part of Khafre remains outside the model. This accounts for the need of a capstone and why one is not presently observed on the Pyramid of Khufu. The reason for this is that the apex of the pyramid referred to as Horus, represents Khufu *without* its capstone. For it is the *apex* of the satellite pyramid of Khufu that represents, or marks, the pyramid apex of the Pyramid of Khufu within this secondary model.

Second, there is a slight (only slight) difference in height between the pyramid Khufu and the Pyramid of Khafre. This is because the tombs are at a slight difference in elevation, as we observed when we deciphered the interior of Khufu. But the most obvious of all is the height ratio of Menkaure. In addition, if one were to stand south of the physical pyramid of Menkaure and aligned oneself correctly, one would witness the identical alignment imagery.

In Chapter 15 we will demonstrate that these locations are as we have stated; once again validated by the full plateau model when constructed.

Note: Traditionally, the dates for the three "pyramid age" Pharaohs are as follows:
- Khufu or Cheops (Greek name) - reigned 2551-2258 BCE
- Khafre, or Ra'kha'ef - reigned 2520 - 2494 BCE.
- Menkaure - reigned 2490 - 2472

All are from the 4th Dynasty and in the period known as the Old Kingdom: 2575 - 2134 BCE.

Chapter 8

Crystal Clear

In this chapter, we will further discuss the blueprint and layout of the Giza Plateau, the global grid, and the subterranean crystals associated with certain "sacred sites" located around the planet.

However, initially we need to have an understanding of the prevailing events that are occurring around the globe. This understanding will lead to a magnificent change on the date of the alignment on December 21, 2012.

Both of the following quotes/prophecies may have reflected the coming and resulting effects of Comet Lee (Comet C/1999 H1Lee):

> *When the sun had gone down and it was dark, behold, a smoking*
> *fire pot and a flaming torch passed between these pieces.*
> — Genesis 15.17

> *When the eclipse of the Sun will then be,*
> *In broad daylight the monster will be seen:*
> *Everyone will differ on the interpretation,*
> *High price unguarded: none will have prepared.*
> — Nostradamus, *The Prophecy*:
> Century 3 Quatrain 34[1]

There have been many interpretations of the Nostradamus quatrains. However, at this point in time we refer to the most relevant concept.

The main issue concerned three anomalous objects observed during the Solar eclipse[2] on August 11, 1999. It is thought that Comet Lee fragmented while on its round trip around the sun. However, the important fact is that with the appearance of Comet Lee, electromagnetic activity increased somewhat, as did the solar flare activity.[2]

Our main concern here is to tie up the information and data we have been consistently attempting to keep up with, and to inform and prepare you, the reader, for what is about to transpire. Surely, many of you have been asking what on earth is happening to our weather of late. Why so many earthquakes? What are those unusual radar rings[3] we keep seeing? What about the fireballs in the skies, many of which had been seen prior to and after the Turkey earthquake[4] and of course the Lunar and Solar anomalies? Not only have these "natural phenomena" been seen and experienced, but recorded on magnetometer charts and seismometer readings at various locations around the globe.[5] In addition, many radar ring anomalies have been witnessed simultaneously around military installations, begging the question: Does HAARP[6] (High Frequency Active Auroral Research Program) have anything to do with this? Perhaps, in part, it may, but we will reveal that there is more to this, much more. During late 1999 and for most part of 2000, strange lights, fireballs in the sky and color blasts have been witnessed.[7] Electromagnetic activity on many of these occasions fluctuated through the roof. These balls of lightning are often associated with the residual effects of inter-dimensional activity.

At approximately 22.18 hours (Cairo time) on December 21, 2012, a highly significant event will occur. An alignment will take place, which will allow the universe to expand to its next stage. Over the next few chapters we will explain the concept of this process and provide evidence supporting this claim.

It is vital that we understand the recent "natural" events that have and will occur in the time leading up to the 2012 date. The more one comprehends the physics of these events, the more quickly and prepared we will become concerning the events that will transpire.

THE GIZA PLATEAU

Deep beneath the plateau, situated among the many subterranean passageways throughout the Thura limestone, is a particular chamber. Located within this chamber is what we will call "The Crystal." This crystal is best described as a machine which, when aligned, forms the constellation of stars as they appeared aeons ago. This alignment of stars then takes in the light, or energy, and re-aligns it back to its original configuration, density and frequency level. This subsequently strengthened band is emitted back out, thus strengthening the grid. We have briefly described, above and elsewhere, the effects of the electromagnetic activity caused by Comet Lee on the working equipment below the plateau. Therefore, whether or not the outer chambers of the Hall of

Records have been breached, it is important to be able to have access to the lower chambers where this crystal lies. The main problem of course, is how we access "The Crystal" in order for it to be re-aligned, so that it reflects and is able to adjust itself in order to compensate for the energy alignment change that has already begun to occur. This change will continue throughout the period leading up to the full alignment on 21st December 2012. Reading this, one's immediate response would be, "What's the rush? We have 12 years before alignment is to occur, not to mention what effect one 'crystal' could have on a whole planet!"

A further point to remember here is the theory of the global grid, where many (crystal) sites are connected in turn to each other. Together, they emanate a powerful earth vortex matrix that includes the possible existence of other smaller crystals, along with the necessary operating equipment. However, in answer to the above response, energy reaches its maximum potential before it progresses to its next highest state. This energy is in the form of light waves. Matter is determined by the density and frequency of this energy, when broken down, and these light waves adhere to the laws, which are dictated by the Time, Space and Matter continuum. This would be not too much of a problem if these light waves were coming at us from a singular direction. *But they are not!*

When we decoded Genesis, we learned that these light waves are coming at us from six different angles. The point at which they meet (where density and frequency are equal as per Time, Space, Matter) is the point where we begin dealing with quanta matter. The same laws of reflection and refraction remain constant, and only become more complex as they are compounded. It is at this stage that the problem occurs. Density and frequency are increasing; however, spatial relationship remains the same. Thus, until such time as the spatial relations are adjusted to reflect the changes in density frequency (on 21st December 2012) the changes must occur internally.

Second: On the electromagnetic spectrum we perceive things on a very narrow band we call visible light spectrum (color). It is only within this spectrum that our Universe exists "to us." There are as many Universes co-existing as there are discernible levels within an extended electromagnetic spectrum. Thus, as such, all dimensions adhere to the same laws (Time, Space, Matter). Closer movement toward maximum alignment creates havoc in the space-separating dimension. Action creates re-action.

The numbers are relatively simple:

Angles	- at start	= 30 degrees	+ Value of 0
Angles	- at end	= 30 degrees	+ Value of 0
Arc Speed -	at start	= 50 degrees	+ Value of 0
Arc Speed -	at end	= 50 degrees	+ Value of 0

The above calculations are derived from work on the Giza-Genesis lineage connection.

Finally, we have to break down our color spectrum (visible), since there are equal opposites in all things. Each half is separated by a definitive point (which we will call 0) with white as the center of the color spectrum. Shades of color are also separated from the next shade (also by a 0). As humans, we rely mainly on water and air; we visualize both in the blue part of the spectrum and exist, most comfortably, within the limits of the shades of blue within the light spectrum.

"The Crystal" is honed into levels of blue which exist within the room in which it is housed. In other words, it is bathed in this blue light. By re-aligning The Crystal, it will slightly alter the color that it is set to break down, i.e., within the blue levels of color. One must bear in mind that The Crystal rests in the exact spot where the three positive light waves intersect dead center.

One of the additional ideas that Genesis (when it was deciphered) showed us, was the progression or "flow" of matter — Adam - Abram - Abraham. Adam is the point from which we began, "a rib extracted from his side." In other words, the Sun takes on a different role, that of Eve, or Mother of our Earth. When Adam's energy flow (directional) intersects with a second source, the combination creates Abram.

When the third energy source is calculated in, it creates Abraham. Adam is our sun, thus a direct flow. The rivers Tigris and Euphrates (in ancient Mesopotamia, now modern Iraq) represent the other two flows of incoming energy. This is represented on the Plateau by the "solar pits" where "solar barques" were discovered. One of these has been reconstructed and housed in a building adjacent to the Great Pyramid.

All of this information is encoded in stone on the Giza Plateau. This was accomplished by the placement of all physical elements (past and present) existing on the plateau, and also encoded in the precision of the measurements in relation to the overall complex.

As previously mentioned, Giza is not the only location where a crystal is present; in fact, a number of these "crystals" are located around the globe. All are placed in exact locations, thus creating and completing an electromagnetic grid system. In addition, tunnel systems that appear to be endless, originate from under the Giza plateau itself and interconnect with many of these sites. At first, these tunnel systems were only identified through Remote Viewing.[8]

Once the twelve houses of Israel have been re-aligned (The Crystal) many other artifacts that are housed under the plateau will emerge. The majority will be positive or beneficial discoveries. However, at least one item does not fall into that category. Thus, once The Crystal is correctly realigned, it will be negated. Since we have won the argument for free will, we are confident this negation will be accomplished.

Included in the items waiting to be discovered are machinery, such as the soul machine, records of our origins, and many other secrets.

Etherian Warriors and the more powerful Etherian Guardians protect access to the site of the crystal. These Etheric Guardians[9] are not to be confused with Etheric Watchers, although both have similar physical descriptions. They are seven to eight feet tall, broad-shouldered and in physical outline similar to humans, with their head size proportionate to the height. They appear "black," or rather, their substance appears to be empty or void, without eyes. Yet they appear to be highly light sensitive.

Etheric Watchers in description are similar to Etherian Guardians, but they are used primarily as observers, since they are very sensitive to colors. They appear to have the ability to absorb colors with which they come into contact, and for which they are specifically on the lookout. These are the colours that are emitted by the aura of humans; our feelings and emotional states emit very discernible color patterns. Fear and aggression are their primary targeted colors. The watchers will attempt to dissuade people from whom these colors are presently emanating, from moving forward. If these attempts fail, the colors are absorbed and filtered out; absorbed into their "void" and sent on, possibly to another dimension where they are utilized as energy.

The Guardians' responsibility is more clearly defined. *No one* gets by unless they have a "key." These keys are generally harmonic or acoustic (verbal), and unless you possess the correct key, you cannot pass the Guardians.

2012, COMET LEE AND THE BIRTH CRITERIA OF OUR NEW NEIGHBOUR

A satellite (or Queen's) pyramid of the Pyramid of Khufu will be the center point for the complete Giza alignment on December 21, 2012, at 22.18 hours (local Cairo time), where the Earth, Sun, Mercury and Venus will be completely aligned.

As stated in the "Crystal Clear" chapter, we are witnessing many anomalous "weather events," including unusual mass solar flare activity, detection of anomalous objects during the recent solar eclipse, formation of a "mystery object" orbiting the sun, fireballs in the skies, earthquakes, and much more.

What has all this to do with the Giza Plateau and our ancient origins on this planet? Plenty. And here we begin to get down to the real "nuts and bolts" issues, whereby we will attempt to explain what is occurring, and what we can expect in the future.

The date of September 21, 1999 was not one pulled out of a hat at random. When we first brought that date to the forefront (over a year ago), we were well aware that on that date an irreversible and non-preventable series of events would begin to unfold. We were right. As predicted, these events began on September 22, 1999.

On April 15 or 16, 1999, Comet 1999 (C/1999 H1 LEE) was detected approaching our solar system. What made this Comet different from most was its declination as it approached and eventually passed through our solar system. Not much was said about this Comet, mainly because, sadly, science today still holds on to the "Big Bang" theory. Certainly this little Comet served as their wake-up call!

Once we had successfully decoded Genesis, the only unknown that remained was the factor that would trigger the series of events leading up to the date of Universal Expansion (December 21, 2012). Enter Comet Lee — right on schedule. Comet Lee was highly instrumental in triggering events towards the Sun's birth of our newest planet. That planet is presently forming inside our very Sun. On December 21, 2000, it will be expelled from the Sun, and find itself in an orbit slightly offset of the orbit of the inner planets that are presently orbiting the Sun within our Solar System.

THE GENESIS CONNECTION

This new planet will continue on its ejected orbital path, while simultaneously continuing to solidify, until – yes, you guessed it! – December 21, 2012. At that time it will shift into the same orbital path along with the other existing inner planets. In the book of Genesis, in the story of Cain and Abel, this event is described as the "birth of Cain."

Once the time of expansion arrives and the criteria are met, thus accommodating Cain's placement within the system, we will call that new location "Abel." Cain then shifts over into this new placement position that will be clearly defined, and is reserved for Abel. "Cain slays Abel" etc.

Science today views electromagnetic interaction as the driving force of our universe. This electromagnetic energy interaction of and with our sun influences our planets. It is traveling outwards from the sun in a wave motion. This particular energy source is one-dimensional, and since we perceive our universe in three dimensions, we must establish the source of the energy (electromagnetic input) that substantiates our existence in this three-dimensional Universe.

Through this inter-weaving process of electromagnetic wave patterns, we define our planets' evolutionary process. These three sources, of which our Sun is only one, are being emitted, or originate from neighboring constellations.

In addition to the maximum arc spread of these three incoming waves, the fixed angle is precisely thirty degrees. (Thirty degrees latitude is the prime latitude for entry for space vehicles from space.) The operational angle is set to a maximum of fifty degrees of arc (remember the measurements of Noah's Ark — width of 50, height of 30). The electromagnetic interaction that occurred between the Sun and Comet Lee as Lee passed by the Sun, at that declination and over that distance, triangulated with an incoming wave pattern from another Sun, in another constellation. This triangulation triggered a controlled area of acceptance within the Sun. However, because we are only approximately 12 years from total alignment (Universal), the influence of the Star in our neighboring constellation will manage to hold this plasma discharge in a tight orbit around the Sun – i.e., versus moving out and away from the Sun, as do most plasma releases. Bear in mind that approximately 12 years in Universal Time is miniscule, and that those two neighboring stars are almost in their alignment positions at this point in time. When those stars move (at the time of alignment) on December 21, 2012, they will push, or pull, that new orbiting body away from the Sun and place it into its new orbit, which is on our orbital plane.

Could the above be interpreted as the same event that Nostradamus referred to as the "First Wave"? We believe this indeed may be the case.

Notes

1. Nostradamus was born in the Provencal city of St. Remy, France in 1503, to a family of Jewish origin. He originally studied medicine, but by 1550 was issuing annual Almanacs and by 1555, published the first edition of the "Centuries.

2. Solar flare activity. *Comet Lee and the Nostradamus Prophecies*, Marshall Masters September 7, 1999

"From the middle of September through the remainder form a closed circuit of sorts. Given that this channel presents a path of less resistance to the Sun than other points on it's surface, this makes us especially vulnerable to the possibility of a Sun storm, or what scientists call a Coronal Mass Ejection (CME).According to NASA, this is impossible. And this, is the main point of contention between NASA's dirty snowball theory and Professor Jim McCanney's Plasma Discharge Theory, which we advocate."

3. Turkey Earthquake. August 17, 1999, 17,000 persons killed and injured tens of thou sands more.

4. National Earthquake information centre — World Data Center for seismology, Denver.Alphabetical listings of all stations at:
    http://wwwneic.cr.usgs.gov/neis/station_book/station_code.html

5. Radar rings. Electromagnetic pulse waves as seen via weather satellites over certain areas, and shown as complete circle formations, or pulses of arrow shaped anomalies.

6. HAARP — High Frequency Active Auroral Research Program.
    HAARP is a scientific endeavour aimed at studying the properties and behaviour of the ionosphere, with particular emphasis on being able to understand and use it to enhance communications and surveillance systems for both civilian and defence.

    The HAARP program is committed to developing a world class ionospheric research facility consisting of:
    ·*The ionospheric research instrument (IRI), a high power transmitter facility operating in* the HF frequency range. The IRI will be used to temporarily excite a limited area of the ionosphere for scientific study.
    ·*Diagnostic instruments that will be used to observe the physical processes that occur into "excited region."*

7. From their web site at: http://w3.nrl.navy.mil/projects/haarp/gen.html

8.   Captain Bruce Cathie; Captain Bruce Cathie was born in 1930 in Auckland, New Zealand, and was educated at Otahuhu Technical College. On leaving school, he became an engineering apprentice, then joined the Royal New Zealand Air Force to train as a pilot. After completing his flying training, he spent three years in agricultural aviation. It was during that time in 1952, that with a group of friends, he made a prolonged evening sighting of a UFO at Mangere, Auckland. This event led to over 30 years of research and the publication of six books detailing his discoveries.

It is now over thirty years ago that Captain Cathie began his investigation into the world electromagnetic grid system. His initial interest was sparked by a sighting of an unidentified flying object over one of the local harbours in Auckland,New Zealand. He was immediately aware that there were machines, other than normally known aircraft, moving through our airspace, which appeared to be more highly advanced technically than our own.

As time went on, it became known to him that many other fellow pilots and radar opera-tors around New Zealand were also sighting similar machines which were carrying out manouvres and flying at speeds that exceeded the capabilities of all known types of air-craft. It became obvious that either our own scientists had very advanced secret knowl-edge or we were possibly being visited by highly advanced beings from outer space. Later, as more information was received, it appeared that both these answers were possible.

— *Mathematics of the World Grid from:*

http://homepages.ihug.co.nz/~brucelc/intro/intro.htm

9.   Remote Viewing — RV. The ability to breach the restrictions of time and space via thought and consciousness. This was a system that was used commonly by the military in the 1970's and 1980's as a form of psychic spying

10. Some may refer to these guardians as Chaldeans, (pronounced Kal-dean), the name origi-nating from ancient groups which once inhabited Mesopotamia (modern Iraq). Mesopotamia means "the land between the two rivers" The Tigris and Euphrates. It is considered that a highly advanced civilisation flourished in this region before ancient Egypt and Greece.

Chapter 9

The Final Countdown!

The following chapter is probably one of the most crucial and important documents that most of you will ever read in this lifetime. Regardless of your beliefs and practices, it is essential that, if nothing else, at least you read the following information. It may have a profound effect on all our lives on this planet.

Is a war going on in the outer reaches of our Solar system? Can we protect planet Earth, which is about to enter the next ascension? And can we avoid being drawn into it? Possibly, if we can attract the attention of certain agencies concerning the correct method of protection laid down under this planet, aeons ago. What are those enormous anomalous objects observed orbiting our sun, and what is their intention?

READ ON—YOU HAVE THE RIGHT TO KNOW

You have read the chapter, "The Genesis Connection," dealing with our true origins on this planet. We further clarified this information in our chapter, "Crystal Clear," concerning the crystal deep below the Giza plateau connected with other global crystals. We then told you about Comet Lee[1] and the criteria for birth of our new neighbor, offering an explanation as to what lately has been going on in our skies. This is essential background for appreciating what we are about to reveal.

It is imperative that you follow this chapter very closely. Read, think and decide for yourselves. This is your planet, and your children's. This is a crucial time for free will and making choices.

When one is dealing with such material as we are presenting here, it is difficult to attempt an explanation according to the normal scientific and generally accepted theories and concepts. Indeed, much of what is about to be revealed has no proper understanding in physics and biology, as we know it today.

What is about to occur? Although the answer may appear bizarre and unbelievable, and some may call this a conspiratorial revelation, the plain simple fact of the matter is that we are about to be drawn into a war of cosmic proportions.

On August 11, 1999,[2] we witnessed the last solar eclipse of that century, and in various countries a number of anomalous objects were observed. It was thought at the time that Comet Lee had fragmented while on its trip around the sun. However, the important fact is that with the appearance of Comet Lee, electromagnetic activity increased, as did the solar flare activity.

In addition, prior to the eclipse, in May, an intriguing crop formation was seen in the UK, representing the very same event that was witnessed on August 11. Was someone somewhere was trying to tell us something?

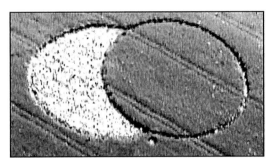

Figure 9.1 - Eclipse Crop Circle

Since that date we have been experiencing many anomalous atmospheric events, severe weather, many earthquakes on or near ancient sacred sites, fireballs and unusual lights in the sky — not to mention the increased sightings of unidentified flying objects.

Not only have these phenomena been witnessed on a global scale, but have been recorded on magnetometer and seismology charts at various locations. As we explained in the "Crystal Clear" chapter, these fireballs and unusual lights in the sky are possibly the reaction to and association of the residual effects of inter-dimensional activity.

In addition, these events are often seen in tandem with high HAARP activity and observation of anomalous radar rings, mainly encircling military installations in North America.

What is going on?

We believe that in a number of instances these events were a process of "targeting," which was completed around November 17, 1999. Also witnessed were the numerous sightings of large black triangular UFO's, materialising in and out of our atmosphere. These are Plasma Target Specific Bombers that are unmanned (drones) devices. They target an area, enter, dump and retreat through their locked vortex portals. However, it is now crucial to understand what has been going on around our sun, and how this will affect our planet and all who dwell on it.

The 'Sun Cruiser' Or 'Orca'

In the latter part of 1998, the Internet began circulating photographs of unusual objects observed around our sun, captured by the SOHO[3] and LASCO satellites, controlled by NASA (National Aeronautical Space Agency). Subsequently, the terms of reference for these anomalies were referred to as the ORCA and the Sun Cruiser, resulting in a feverish "search for the real truth" campaign by a number of dedicated and serious researchers[3].

On September 22, 1999, an extremely unusual anomaly emerging from the sun was observed on one of the LASCO satellites, which soon after "went down" and remained down for some time. This pulse beam effect was affectionately termed as some form of Stargate, which was analyzed in order to find out exactly what this anomaly comprised of. We glossed over this in the "2012 Comet Lee" chapter.

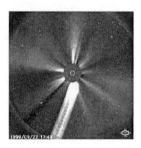

Figure 9.2 - Solar Stargate

We now arrive at the most crucial hypothesis of this whole affair, and as you will see, it may in fact turn out to be much more than pure conjecture. THIS IS HAPPENING RIGHT NOW, and we can no longer ignore the evidence that is materializing before our very eyes.

Those anomalous objects (termed Sun Cruisers — and there are now at least two) are in fact Plasma Carriers, of gigantic proportions, said to be in excess of three thousand miles across! The carriers will initiate an artificial disturbance within the sun, causing the sun to eject two massive Coronal Mass Ejections (CME's). The trajectory of these CME's will be directed at Earth, at which time all satellites will be placed out of commission, as will the entire power grid. It is at this point that we, too, will enter into the war with the

Draconians. BELIEVE IT! The Draconions are led by one who is often referred to as Draco.[5] We chose to use "Draconians" as the name given to the dark or evil side involved in this conflict. Much of the information was "corroborated" by Remote Viewing techniques from two independent Remote Viewers. Additional information on this area will be provided in Volume Two of the series.

As described above, many anomalous radar rings have been observed on satellite weather channels over North America, all of which seem to be associated with, and protecting, a number of military installations in areas such as Nellis Naval strategic weapon FAC, Fort Knox, "Area 51" ("Dreamland"), Standiford USAF . . . the list goes on. These appear to be attempts, utilizing electromagnetic field shielding, to protect from minor incoming cometary debris and other objects of unknown origin. However, this will have no effect whatsoever on the direct massive CME deployment!

The exact timing of the "attack" is not known, but from information relayed to us, it appears to be very soon. Communication was terminated before an exact date could be established. All we have is the "transmission" of "Wednesday, Thursday, Wednesday, Thursday" (repeated). Due to the increase in the electromagnetic field around the globe, it seems that communication is very difficult to maintain.

When the initial assault begins, the Plasma Carrier will move closer to earth. As of this moment, we predict that this will occur after the Birth Event stipulated December 21, 2000 — for it will be at this time that the "Crystal Grid" will become ineffective.

Certainly, we want to know more. Why is this occurring and who is the aggressor? The answer, as to be expected is complex, and one that extends way back in time on this planet. To acquire a brief background on this, a re-read of "The Genesis Connection" may be helpful. We have to look to our true origins on this planet to find an answer, and as our time for a full explanation is very limited, we will merely point out the following.

We, on earth, are a combination of races from several worlds, where the soul migrates from one place to another within a given time frame. Our strongest representation on this planet are the Pleiadians, or Plejarians. The Pleiades is a star cluster situated in the constellation of Taurus, approximately 450-500 light years distant, in the time frame as we know it. However, the majority of the existing souls on this plane were placed here during the last ascension. Thus, it is the work of Thoth, the ancient Egyptian god of wisdom, that is of the utmost importance. Thoth has noted and logged each soul and monitored its progress over time. Therefore, to make ascension, one has to be preferably "selected" as an individual and not as a group.

Aeons ago, a "deal" was struck with the Galactic Council, originally because at some previous time, the Plejarians had all but eradicated the reptilian life forms from the surface of this planet. The Plejarians have since lived and existed under a completely different belief system, e.g., light verses dark.

The next question I hear you asking is, WHY? And exactly WHAT do THEY want?

They are here to procure the already harvested resources. They require your soul (remember the Giza soul machine) — the pure energy of souls. They do not wish to give people the opportunity to make that ascension into the new time frame that is about to occur.

In the previous chapters, "The Genesis Connection" and "Comet Lee," we explained how we arrived at the date of December 21, 2012, also known as the Mayan end count,[6] and its importance. At this time the universe will begin to expand and all universal bodies will evolve to their next state. Whether the form is passive or negative depends upon their immediate relationships to their respective sources. Some will move to their second, third or fourth levels, while others will come under the influences of new (secondary) sources. Because the progression is linear, this time frame will have come full circle. However, it is important to note that this time frame will always exist because it justifies the existence of the next time frame. To illustrate this point, we may take the example of the computer system used in the Phoenix Projects.[7] If the system utilized time (zero time) as at the center of the galaxy, that time frame will not exist past December 21, 2012. Those of you who have knowledge of Remote Viewing techniques will appreciate the problems involved in "viewing" beyond that date. Subsequently, they will not be able to vortex beyond that date.

It is possible, but not recommended, to vortex through time frames connecting the two. This is a highly dangerous activity, such as occurred during the Philadelphia Experiment.[8] Therefore, to possess this knowledge, combined with the ability to implement it, would be earth's best defense system.

To put this into perspective, would you send an attack force to a planetary system, knowing that the force may be re-routed and vortexed in time — while simultaneously knowing that at zero time there is no point of reference with which to calculate your exit? Sheer suicide. Shades of *Stargate*,[9] one may think?

Thus, this time change event is the reason for the acceleration of the war that is happening presently just beyond Jupiter in our solar system, and which is beginning to escalate; consequently drawing planet earth into the conflict.

Apparently, this conflict is between (for lack of a better description) the Inter-Galactic Federation and the Sirian group. It also involves the Draconians and Orions.

Many thousands of years ago, Earth was invaded by a reptilian race (possibly from the Draco constellation) that arrived in a gigantic carrier (similar to our Plasma Beam Carrier). Ultimately, settlers of the Lyrian Empire drove this race from the surface of the earth, and the remaining attackers went subterranean. They stayed there in stasis until a time when they would be "re-activated" by an incoming ship, such as the passing of Comet Lee and subsequent anomalous objects observed orbiting our sun.

Aeons ago, deals were made, which still remain valid today, between our forefathers and the "Council" or Federation, which prohibit unsolicited intervention by outside members' allies. Unsolicited, yes — but who on this planet has the authority to ask on our behalf?

How can Mother Earth be Protected?

A natural defense exists, comprised of the Global Grid of crystals situated on and under ancient sites around our planet. We will describe this Global Grid in greater detail below. There is also a possibility that, if for some reason the work by some of our "scientists" has put us into a time lock, we may ask for "outside" assistance. However, this scenario is governed by our explanation regarding unsolicited assistance.

The Crystal Global Grid was placed and instigated at the many ancient sacred sites located around our planet. These were artificially laid down thousands of years ago for the purpose of stabilization, and also, to form a protective "shield." The focal point of the Crystal Global Grid is the Giza Plateau. Many other secondary crystals exist at the other ancient sites, including Stonehenge, Mexico, Easter Island, New Grange (Ireland), Green Stone Trail (New Zealand), and others.

If one were to look up recent earthquake activity, one would find a correlation and connection to these "sacred sites."

As we explained in the "Crystal Clear" chapter, the centrally located crystal lies deep beneath the Pyramid complex on the Giza Plateau, Cairo, and adjacent to what some refer to as Hall of Records. This is the crucial crystal that needs to be re-aligned in order to stabilize the earth's core. Once this has been carried out, all other crystals should re-align.

It is imperative that this crystal be aligned, in order to afford planet Earth the protection she needs for imminent incoming. And here's the good news: This Crystal and associated machinery have now been activated!

In the next few chapters we will explain how and when this was accomplished.

Notes

1. Comet Lee effects can be researched at the millennium group's Internet site at: http://www.millenngroup.com/repository/cometary/cometary.html

2. Although the solar eclipse of 1999 occurred in August, accompanied with three unidentified anomalies observed while the sun was actually eclipsed, on April 15th a crop circle appeared in a field in England reflecting the very san\me occurrence. This may be seen on the Internet at: http://members.aol.com/phikent/orbit/bitback43.html

3. SOHO. The Solar and Heliospheric Observatory, a project being carried out by the European Space Agency and NASA. The satellites were launched on December 2, 1995, and their purpose is to monitor the solar activities of our sun. While LASCO, stands for Large Angle and Spectrometric Coronagraph Experiment. It is one of 11 instruments. A coronagraph is a telescope that is designed to block light coming from the solar disk, in order to see the extremely faint emission from the region around the sun, called the corona.

4. "Rusty" and 'Flash" are well known Radar anomaly researchers, their websites may be found at: http://www.geocities.com/Heartland/Garden/2733/menu.html and at: http://www.toledolink.com/~flash/flashx.html

5. From the constellation of Draco (Dragon). "The Monstrous Dragon of the Cosmic War" It was said Draco represents the dragon who guarded the golden apples in the garden of the Hesperides. One of the labours of Hercules as to steal these apples (some sources state it was his eleventh labour, others the twelfth.

6. 2012 - *The How and Why of the Mayan End Date in 2012.* John Major Jenkins.

> *Why did the ancient Mayan or pre-Maya choose December 21st, 2012 A.D., as the end of their Long Count calendar? This article will cover some recent research. Scholars have known for decades that the 13-baktun cycle of the Mayan "Long Count" system of timekeeping was set to end precisely on a winter solstice, and that this system was put in place some 2300 years ago. This amazing fact - that ancient - can skywatchers were able to pinpoint a winter solstice far off into the future - has not been dealt with by Mayanists. And why did they choose the year 2012? One immediately gets the impression that there is a very strange mystery to be confronted here. I will be building upon a clue to this mystery reported by epigrapher Linda Schele in Maya Cosmos.*

7. Project Phoenix is the world's most sensitive and comprehensive search for extraterrestrial intelligence. However, there was another more sinister project involving Mind control Invisibility, Worm Holes/Space Time and time Travel. This evolved from the Montauk research project, involving Teleportation, and treaties with the Grays, Pleiadians, and the Reptilians.

8. Philadelphia Experiment. A "radar invisibility" research project that arose out of Project Rainbow during World War 2.

> *Project Rainbow was allegedly an experiment conducted upon a small destroyer escort ship during World War II, both in the Philadelphia Naval Yard and at sea; the goal was to make that ship invisible to enemy detection. The accounts vary as to whether the original idea was to achieve invisibility to enemy radar or whether the prize sought after was more profound: optical invisibility. Either way, it is commonly believed that the mechanism involved was the generation of an incredibly intense magnetic field around the ship, which would cause **refraction** or bending of light or radar waves around the ship, much like a mirage created by heated air over a road on a summer day. The legend goes on to say that the experiment was a complete success... except that the ship actually disappeared physically for a time, and then returned. They wanted to "cloak" the ship from view, but they got de-materialization and teleportation instead.*

From The Philadelphia Experiment A-Z at: http://www.wincom.net/softarts/philexp.html

9. SG 1. Originally a film and now a successful Television series, Stargate, or SG-1. A large circular 'gate' is discovered in Egypt, and by utilising the various hieroglyphs inscribed on the perimeter, one is able to 'dial up' a planet in the same or different time-space continuum.

Chapter 10

The Erideans

Who are they and where do they originate?

We mentioned in Chapter 9, "The Final Countdown," that these anomalous objects observed orbiting the sun were in fact "Plasma Carriers," and possibly of Eridean origin. However, there seems to be an additional object/accompanied object, which may be of a different design.

In that chapter we also presented the thesis that our planet is made up of a number of races that inhabited earth many millions of years ago, of which the Pleiadian group was the main representative. Prior to and long after the Pleiadians, other races were involved in the genetic integration of the inhabitants of earth. Thus, the real "make-up" of our genetic ancestry may never be completely known. As a starting point, let us take a brief view of the origins and social structure of the Erideans to learn about the role they are playing out in this scenario. Remember, the present scenario that is unfolding has a highly complex background, and therefore, in some circumstances, complete details may not be available. However, for the benefit of those who wish to comprehend what is transpiring, we submit the following.

WHO ARE THE ERIDEANS?

Initial contact seems to portray the Erideans as "Reptoid Klingons" (as observed in the series "Startrek") for want of a better description, but without the physical fighting qualities of that class.

"They appear to follow the reptoid pattern of having little logical brain and are controlled by spirit.[1] It is apparent that this is the first time they have encountered man in its present form, and thus they do not comprehend the human race. What's new, I hear you ask!

One common denominator exists between them and "us," and that is the interest in an old enemy . . . The Anunnaki.[2] It appears that they are still looking for them. Perhaps this is their motive in orbiting our sun — to await the Anunnaki! If indeed this is the case, then we could very shortly bear witness to and even become drawn into a "final conflict."

WHERE DO THE ERIDEANS ORIGINATE?

The Erideans are a completely telepathic race and seem to originate from the constellation of Eridanus. This constellation is represented as a long, winding river that starts at the left foot of Orion in the north, sweeps south of Taurus, west to the edge of Cetus, then doubles back east to Caelum; eventually culminating far to the south, at the border with Hydrus. It is difficult to identify which river the constellation represents. Some writers claimed it was the Tigris or Euphrates, others the Nile. The constellation is situated approximately10.7 to 12- plus light years to the near groups, which include Eridanus Delta and Epsilon.

Epsilon is very similar to our earth, and its sun is in the same class. The Delta planet is said to be a "carboniferous" (agricultural) planet that possessed diamonds as ubiquitous as is quartz; and which to them are as decorative as are rocks on planet Earth. Delta is inhabited by reptoids that look fairly human. However, their sun is a "variable" star, so they also employ complete weather control. This enables the inhabitants to live in windowless stone houses, or possibly reinforced concrete, as we know it.

The Erideans are also referred to as Cetians, or Tau Cetians, a human race of Mediterranean or South American origin, and of tan-skinned appearance. These are said to be in alliance with the Pleiadians, who have formed a "Cetian alliance" with others, in a desire to establish a common defense against their reptilian nemesis. It is thought that the Erideans are reluctant to make contact, since the telepathic noise we create would upset them greatly. In addition, our gravity is uncomfortable for them, causing a risk of bacterial or virus contamination.

By our standards, the Erideans may perhaps appear slightly reptilian, and therefore, any contact would have to be controlled. If they do wish to make contact, it would be at a distance without a physical landing. Also, because of their complete telepathic abilities, they may not appreciate our normal methods of communication, including radio and television etc. It is possible that these Eridean Plasma Carriers are part of a fleet that is involved in a galactic dispute beyond Jupiter.

In summing up, therefore, it is conceivable that an alliance may be possible with this group, since they appear friendlier than the Anunnaki.

A number of diverse reptilian races, both good and bad, are distributed throughout equally diverse galaxies and universes. The Draconians, for instance, who originate from the constellation of Draconis, almost entered our solar system from the "companion" to the Hale Bopp[3] comet in 1997. However, it was believed they were prevented by the Galactic Federation from doing so. Otherwise it would have been a case of "Jurassic Park," where earth would have provided the best "restaurant in the Galaxy."

From Sirius[4] we have the red group, the Sirians. This is the group that is involved in the war beyond Jupiter. The Sirians once inhabited and "ruled" Earth prior to 15,000 BCE in Atlantis. Sirius appears to be the epicenter of the Ashtar or Astarte collective, where humanoids of various types, Sasquatch, Reptiloids, Greys, and Reptilian hybrid species seem to have collated together in the past.

Previously, the Sirians have waged war with the Orion Empire or the "Unholy Six" reptilian star systems in the Orion open cluster. The ancient dispute is over "landlordship" of a sector of space containing 21 star systems. This space includes the most strategic star system, SOL, and particularly, planet Earth, Terra or Shan — which is a virtual cosmic "oasis" of water, mineral, plant, animal and genetic resources of incredible variety, compared with most other worlds.

This dispute between the Sirians and Orion reptilians dates back to the ancient invasion of Orion by the Draconian Empire. At that time many "Nordic" type humanoids escaped to Procyon[5] Sol, Sirius and elsewhere. The war in Sirius-B is gravitating towards the Sol System, since one of the major issues of dispute between the two, or three, warring factions (Evadamic-Draconian) is the agenda for this system.

However, as previously mentioned, the Anunnaki is the race to be most wary of — to say the least! Who are they? We on earth are said to be genetically and symbolically part of an off-planet civilization known as the Anunnaki. Thought to originate in the constellation of Lyra,[6] these were the first "creator gods" who knew how to create matter, such as planets, stars, life forms for themselves, and eventually others.

The Lyran's physical lifetimes lasted for approximately one thousand years. In time, however, as their life span decreased, they sought out a substance that would enable them to live longer. They discovered that gold not only increased their longevity, but also provided them with a superconductivity that gave them the ability to be highly telepathic and experience their multidimensionality. Eventually, they spread out into the cosmos and created new civilizations. A few went to Vega, others to the Pleiades, and still others, to Sirius. However, their need for gold was paramount.

The Anunnaki were said to be tall and have been called the Nordics or Blondes, emanating a golden aura. Their symbol is the Winged Disc,[7] which not only represents their starship Nibiru, but is also symbolic of the ability of the spirit to fly free while remembering its wise, divine source.

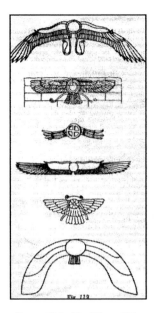

Figure 10.1 - The Winged Disc

These Anunnaki were later called the Elohim (gods) and Nefilim (those who descended). Upon completion of a number of genetic experiments in which they created other races, eventually they produced the hybrid Homo sapiens — us. The souls of those who became human came to earth by their own free will to experience physicality. Several other extraterrestrial civilizations contributed their own input into human DNA and created many races of humans, some of which have now left Earth.

Thus, the Anunnaki could be said to be pattern makers, the creators of archetypes and of the template for human life on Earth. One of the Anunnaki leaders was Enlil (also known as Jehovah). Enlil and Enki were half brothers through the same father, Anu, who was the "king" of this Anunnaki group.

Enlil did not want humans to be equal to them; Enki, on the other hand, was in favor of human freedom and equality. Thus, in order to ensure that humans would be able to benefit from their ancestry, Enki (the serpent of wisdom and healing) suggested that those who came to be called Adam and Eve should eat from the Tree of Knowledge. This subterfuge enraged Enlil who, from that point onward, continued to punish humanity whenever they were close to coming to an answer about life itself, thus seeking to reclaim their rightful heritage. *(See Chapter 2, "The Genesis Connection," for more on this subject.)*

It is believed that both Enki and Enlil, and later their offspring, created many civilizations and religions. Enki and his lineage developed Egypt, but these civilizations rarely had long periods of peace. It is thought that Enlil irradiated Sodom and Gomorrah off the face of the Earth, and Atlantis sank, due to the Anunnaki's experiments with sound technology. The last great flood, approximately 13,000 years ago, became a legend when Enki went against the other Anunnaki and saved humans, the Noahs of earth; Enlil wished to destroy them.

Mars also had a civilisation that was developed by the Anunnaki. Eventually, and possibly after the Exodus, other Anunnaki left the earth, and their secrets of transforming gold into the powerful substance that allowed their longevity, also vanished. In time, humans who remembered, died or disappeared. The knowledge was lost. And yet, people kept trying to capture that special essence of gold in the form of statues, mistakenly believing it was their key to immortality.

Today, it is debatable as to whether the Anunnaki would be able to adapt to our planet's environment. However, the main advantage of the Anunnaki, like the Erideans, their telepathic ability, may also be their downfall or Achilles heel. A telepathic society will have crime, but also little free will. In general, we humans do, at least, have this choice of free will. Corruption or enlightenment? You choose!

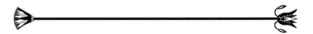

Notes

1.   Viking Remote Viewing – Edmund   Meadows: http://www.viking-z.org/edit2.htm

> *Remote viewing is a new name for an old ability. Remote viewing is the ability of a person to project their conscious observation to a distant location to see or sense what is there. Distance is no object as even the stars are within reach. It was rediscovered and used by the Russians in the 1960s. The Americans rediscovered it around 1970. Now every other intelligence agency is using it to flesh out data from other sources. Remote viewing violates all the moral codes of science and religion. The occult is no better as too much information is withheld. It can be classified as either psychokinetics or a secular path to enlightenment or both*

2. Anunnaki. According to some, Humans are genetically, symbolically

3. As information supplied by Robert Trebor in mails and notes.

4. On July 23, 1995 an unusually bright comet, outside of Jupiter's orbit (7.15 AU!) was discovered independently by Alan Hale, New Mexico and Thomas Bopp, Arizona. The new comet, designated C/1995 O1, is the farthest comet ever discovered by amateurs and appeared 1000 times brighter than Comet Halley did at the same distance. Normally, comets are inert when they are beyond the orbit of Jupiter, so it has been speculated that Comet Hale-Bopp is either a rather large comet or experienced a bright out burst (or both). The comet is the brightest comet since Comet West in 1976. From Hubble Space Telescope images, the comet's diameter has been determined to be about 40 km. The Pic du Midi Observatory has ascertained from their observations that the comet's rotation rate is 11.4 hours. 3. As information supplied by Robert Trebor in mails and notes. From: http://www.jpl.nasa.gov/comet/

5. Sirius in the constellation of Canis Major. The star Sirius (also known as the "Dog star") was known many years ago to the Dogon tribe, located in western Africa (Mali). In the Dogon mythology they say that have had contact with extraterrestrials (reptile like). And in their astronomical knowledge they already knew the existence of Sirius B, a sister/ brother star of the star Sirius. The Dogon tribe knew already that Sirius B orbits Sirius and that an orbit takes around fifty years, without any technical tools.

6. Procyon is the Alpha star in the constellation of Canis minor, the smaller dog. Procyon is just behind Rigel in Orion.

7. The constellation of Lyra, the name of which originated from the Lyre (a stringed instru ment like a harp) which was said to have been invented by Hermes as a gift to his half-brother Apollo, who gave it to Orpheus, the musician of the Argonauts. The main star of Lyra is Vega, or the Harp star.

8. Although the winged disc emblem is often associated with the emblem of the Annunaki, it is also known to Egytpologists as the "winged Sun disc". It is a symbol originating in Assyria and Egypt and has been used by a variety of groups such as Freemasonry, Spiritists, Theoso phy, the Rosicrucians and the Bible Students. This symbol has been known by numerous names such as the winged globe, winged-solar-disk, sun's disc, etc.
    This symbol originated with the Assyrians but is most identified with the Egyptians.and is found in numerous forms on temples in Egypt.

    Emblematic of the element of air, this consists of a circle or solar-type disk enclosed by a pair of wings. In ritual magic it is suspended over the altar in an easterly direction and used when invoking the protection and co-operation of the sylphs.

    Practical Egyptian Magic by Murray Hope.

Chapter 11

The Great Experiment -
The Plan and Purpose

In previous chapters we looked at the background as to what is transpiring in and on the outer reaches of our solar system, and who is involved. Now let us look for an explanation as to why these events are unfolding at this time.

"The Experiment"

Approximately 500,000 years ago, Terra (planet Earth) experienced a severe orbital displacement problem, due to a glancing blow from a passing meteorite. This resulted in a rapidly decaying orbit. Failure to control this event would have created a ripple effect on neighboring stars, in addition to other neighboring orbiting celestial bodies. This is not unlike the rapidly approaching situation in which we now find ourselves.

Thus was the scenario that brought in the involvement of the Galactic Federation. In an unprecedented move, the Federation called upon its planetary members to devise a solution to eliminate or control this imminent problem. The very nature of this potential orbital disaster required considerable scientific and physical expertise in order to implement and accomplish the necessary rescue. Because of the complexity of this task, a number of worlds became involved.

At this time, the Anunnaki inhabited planet Earth, and they readily welcomed the opportunity to help. Therefore, concessions were agreed upon between the Anunnaki and the Federation, and the co-ordinated effort of planetary stabilization began. It was during this time that the peoples from various worlds were ascended and placed on this new developing world. This included the peoples from our own planet Mars.

The procedure involved the laying out and setting of a number of crystals located below strategically aligned sites throughout the globe, with the main focal crystal at the Giza Plateau — the site of the Pyramid complex. Thus, crystals were placed at many of what today we call "ancient sacred sites," including Easter Island, Stonehenge, White Pyramids of China, Machu Pichu, (Peru) Uxmal Pyramid (Mexico), Chichen Itza (Mexico) and others.

It is interesting to note that over recent months a number of earthquakes have been witnessed on or around the majority of these sites. In addition, when we wrote the chapter "2012 Comet Lee," we placed emphasis on the date of December 21, 2012. This is also the time frame (2011/2012) when it is calculated that Earth will be in the mainstream of the much discussed Photon Belt.[1] It was reported that Earth entered the sphere of influence of this belt in 1962.

Every 26,000 years or so, our solar system completes a circuit around the point of origin of our sun, Alcyone, in the Pleiades group. In 2012, we shall be nearing this point once more. Although the energy of this Photon Belt is said by some to be more etheric and spiritual rather than physical in nature, it does in fact interact with the physical aspect surrounding our galaxy.

Naturally the implementation of the plan to stabilize the planet Earth took some time, and upon completion, an unforeseen problem surfaced with regard to the work force that participated in the process. The diverse races from the equally diverse worlds that were involved in the work had come under the influence of our planet's gravity field. Under the circumstances there was a possibility that they could have been removed and ultimately re-adjusted to the gravity fields of other planets. However, there was an alternative solution.

Federation members agreed to initiate an "experiment" that is still presently "floating in the wind." The ultimate aim of this "experiment" was to see if the various races, with varying belief structures, could not only mutually co-exist on a planet, but also safely monitor the evolution of such an attempt.

The whole world spoke the same language, using the same words.

— Genesis 11.1

Also . . .

Then the LORD said, "If now, while they are one people,
all speaking the same language,
they have started to do this,
nothing will later stop them from doing
whatever they presume to do."

— Genesis 11.6

Ultimately, three entities were mutually chosen to oversee the progress of this experiment. Periodically over time as we know it, these entities made themselves available through indirect intervention to assist and guide the peoples of earth. Under the original experimental guidelines, direct intervention was not allowed.

The three representatives, or council members, were not a permanent part of this original plan, a fact that only came about at a later date. In part this was due to a malicious act which the Pleiadians created, and perhaps one about which they now feel ashamed. Possibly they are looking for a way in which to make amends. The unique feature of this experiment was that the entities, or souls, were held in containment within the protective belt they had helped to construct. The redistribution of these souls was aided by the siting of monoliths on the moon, which in turn were connected to the working machinery deep below the Giza Plateau, where the soul-distribution was handled directly. To ensure that all data was recorded correctly, Thoth[2] was given the responsibility and authority to keep track of and document the records of progression, or regression as the case may be, of each soul. Thoth was also given the added responsibility of helping the soul in its search for fulfilment, realization and guidance toward an understanding of the overall picture. Each soul is viewed and recorded by the entity every time physical death occurs. Upon death, the slate is cleared, so to speak, and the soul is sent out again, in order to learn from past life experiences and difficulties. In this manner, the soul is ultimately to attain fulfillment. Some may recall these experiences and the teaching that transpires.

Thoth has also been given the authority to keep alive and further develop the levels of understanding as they relate to the realm of the sciences. This was perceived as important, considering the mix of races involved in the experiment, whereby each race brought a diverse history, culture and science as understood by their individual historical evolution, as well as their own unique personal and cultural beliefs.

It is believed that through time, these cultural differences could have been molded into a common set of understanding, whereby each race could find its own place within the newly integrated system. At the same time, the individual would eventually comprehend that it should not dwell on the past, for this not only retards the growth of the individual, but the group as a whole. Indeed, considerable progress has been made toward realizing this scenario.

However, there have also been many setbacks. When tracing the history of several races cohabiting in the same world, one encounters similar experiences concerning the challenge of establishing of harmonious relations. Nevertheless, it could also be true that after aeons of time and development of cultures, both "spiritually" and physically, these inter-racial differences may now have ceased to exist.

However, on the positive side, we here on Earth have only a few years remaining – between now and December 21, 2012, *to get it right.* This scenario now becomes even more complex, based on the knowledge that the Draconians have set their sights on controlling this section of the Galaxy! Simply put, as outlined in "The Final Countdown," war is headed in our direction. The thought of a negative ending to this scenario has caused some races to look at the possibility of coming to Planet Earth to extract their own people. However, one major factor is being overlooked: We still have those remaining years. *We* have created our own civilization. *We* have made major strides forward and continue to do so at an accelerated rate of progress. Hence, now is when we should enter The Hall of Records and find out just how far, in fact, we *have* come.

WHO MAY ASK?

We mentioned in "Final Countdown" who, or under what circumstances, one should ask for assistance in re-aligning the main crystal below the Giza Plateau. In the following section we will demonstrate the background, method and hazards of implementing such an alignment.

When the experiment was instigated, a certain amount of genetic engineering was carried out to assist integration of the DNA from the various races currently inhabiting earth. This was performed over a period of time so as to allow certain races to overcome the problems related to gravitational and atmospheric conditions. Once equilibrium had been achieved between the gene structure and the DNA, the code was then set. This is what some refer to as the "blessing." The original blessing was ultimately handed down, or passed along from generation to generation, always carried by *one* individual.

This blessing was "carried" in the center of the femur, and in addition, was delivered to the one who has in their possession this DNA the sole right to access the crystal. With this right, the bearer was the only one who could approach the crystal in order to re-align and advance the setting, thereby stabilizing the planet's core. According to Genesis, the act of passing on the blessing consisted of placing the recipients' right hand under the left femur of their predecessor. Therefore, from that point, the recipients carry the weight of this responsibility.

Genesis 25:24

When the time of her delivery came, there were twins in her womb.

Genesis 25:25

> *The first to emerge was reddish, and his whole body was like a hairy mantle: so they named him Esau.*

Genesis 25:26

> *His brother came out next, gripping Esau's heel; so they named him Jacob, Isaac was sixty years old when they were born.*

To illustrate the relevance, and indeed the urgent need for crystal alignment as described in previous articles, a recent occurrence, experienced by one of our group members will be described below.

On October, 1999, late evening, one of our colleagues was visually confronted — a face-to-face confrontation — with a reptilian species. This reptilian was attempting to make definite telepathic communication. After a long period of what may be termed a "frontal staring down," our colleague was shown a picture consisting of two DNA strands. These two strands were almost identical apart from the lower one being green in color[3] and the upper strand a violet color. The name of this reptilian species was *Esau!* A week or so later, our colleague was wakened from sleep by a sharp pain in the upper middle part of his left femur. It was believed that some one, or something, had remotely extracted the DNA from the center of the femur bone. It was assumed that this procedure was carried out for, or by, Esau himself, and seen as an attempt to give him access to the crystal, in order to make changes to the earth's shield. However, instead of advancing the crystal, it was his plan to set it back, thus creating a change in atmosphere that would then allow the Anunnaki to once again walk freely on this planet.

Esau still finds himself unable to access the crystal, since he is still missing the *harmonic* "key." It must be remembered that he swore that he would return to claim that which he believes is his by birthright. But it is a right that he himself willingly gave up.

Genesis 25:30

> *He said to Jacob, "Let me gulp down some of that red stuff. I'm starving."*

Genesis 25:31

> *But Jacob replied, "First give me your birthright in exchange for it."*

Genesis 25:32

> *"Look," said Esau, "I'm on the point of dying. What good will any birthright do me?"*

Genesis 25:33

> *But Jacob insisted, "Swear to me first!" So he sold Jacob his birthright under oath.*

Genesis 25:34

> *Jacob then gave him some bread and the lentil stew; and Esau ate, drank, got up, and went his way. Esau cared little for his birthright.*

WHERE ARE THE ANUNNAKI NOW?

It appears, as learned from a number of sources, that recently the Anunnaki were located in the area known as the "Badlands" of the asteroid belt (a band of asteroids orbiting the sun between Mars and Jupiter). However, they now seem to be itinerant, or "on the run." It is also reported that the Erideans orbiting the sun in their Plasma Carrier or Sun Cruiser, have captured a number of the Anunnaki, who no doubt will be enslaved. This scenario will probably affect their cloaking ability, and soon we may observe evidence of their existence.

More recent reports suggest that "Esau" (Anunnaki) appears to be located on Pluto and involved in a "conference," in an attempt to gain assistance from the Nordics and other races. The Anunnaki still seem to maintain that Planet Earth is their property and they are loathe to give up claims to be the "master race of earth."

Desperation seems to be the attitude at present. During this conference on Pluto, the Anunnaki attempted to enlist the help of a dwarf race from a parallel dimension. Apparently, this race is normally called in when there is "dirty work" to be carried out!

However, coming back to Earth with a literal bump, further investigation seems to point to the location of a small number, a "reconnaissance party," deep below the Giza area in Cairo. Apparently this group slid in under cover of the extended Cairo smog incident of around October 26, 1999. Although the news archives on the Internet regarding this incident have now been deleted, we submit the quotes below regarding this incident.

Quote by an accountant, Mohammed Abdel Monayin, in the daily *Al-Gumhuriya*, circa week of October 27:

> *What is strange is that we have been given no explanation about the nature of this smoke. We demand a plausible explanation.*

Egyptian President Hosni Mubarak commented:

> *There may be something in the atmosphere, or weather conditions may be sometimes very tough there.*

Prior to this event, on October 11, 1999, Cairo suffered the effects of a 5.2 earthquake, of which the epicenter was located in the desert, southeast of Cairo. Of interest to note, there was also an earthquake a few days prior in Sinai. (05Oct1999 05:44:36.5 29.0N 34.9E 10 ML=4.8 M ISR EGYPT)

An additional "coincidence" was the start of the military exercise Bright Star, carried out in Egypt from October 12 through November 3.

For the first time — an intriguing point to note – the military utilized long-haul satellite communications for this exercise, employing 70 members of the contingent of signals from the 11th Signal Brigade.

EXERCISE BRIGHT STAR - EGYPT

Was the military expecting a major incoming – and thus, was geared up for a major force, when — unknown to them — a reconnaissance force slid quietly through the environmental smog event? We suggest that in fact this was the case!

The important factor here is that the Anunnaki were hell-bent on aligning the crystal below Giza for their own ends, in order to establish a planet that would be "environmentally friendly" to their personal needs.

Agencies know of the location of this crystal and are able to access it. However, they do not comprehend its purpose or method, since the crystal is DNA-activated.

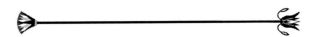

Notes

1.   A photon is a quantum of light, or the smallest possible packet of light at a given wavelength. It is emitted by an atom during a transition from one energy state to another. The photon belt is reportedly a band of intense photon (light) energy that is said to be on a collision course with Earth. If this report is correct, there will be problems with electrical supply, photon energy conversion devices, and increase in psychic abilities for many humans as the transformation of our bodies goes into higher dimensions. The Photon belt was first predicted to arrive by the end of 1996, this date has now passed and there seems less interest in this matter than previously.

Aproximately every 25,000 to 26,000 years our solar system completes one orbit around the central sun of the Pleiades (Alcione—see diagram last page). Ancient Eastern wisdom knows this cycle as the various Yugas. This orbit has a point closest to Alcione and one farthest away from it. The furthest point from the central sun—symbolizing Light—correlates with ignorance. Here Man's consciousness is "in the dark." The nearest point correlates with what we term an awakening or Enlightenment. Alcione is known to the East as Brahma, the seat of creative power or universal magnetism (concerning our particular universe.)

In 1961 science discovered, by means of satellites, a photon belt encircling the Pleiades. This photon belt circles the Pleiadian system at an absolute right angle to its orbital planes. As our sun (and we with it) orbits the Pleiades once every 25,860 years, it reaches the midpoint of the photon belt approximately every 12,500 years. It requires some 2,000 years to traverse it, meaning that after departing this realm, another 10,500 years pass before our Solar System enters it again.

Cosmic Birth: Photon Belt - From, *Connecting Link Magazine # 24. Article entitled A Cosmic Birth by Peter O. Erbe* (14 Oct 1994)

2.   Thoth (identified as Benjamin in Genesis), whose animal was an Ibis or dog-headed baboon was an ancient Egyptian deity. The original Ogdoad of Hermopolis were called 'the souls of Thoth.' Thoth was created by the power of utterance and was called the inventor of speech. He was said to have been 'self-begotten,' having appeared at the dawn of time on a lotus flower. One of his greatest services to Re, was the retrieval of his eye, and as a reward Re created the moon for Thoth. He was also called the 'measurer of time,' and said to be inventor of mathematics, astronomy and engineering, and as such was the accountant to the gods and the secretary of Re. It is said his silver boat transported the souls of the dead across the night sky.

> *"Benjamin is a ravenous wolf; mornings he devours the prey, and evenings he distributes the spoils."* (Genesis 49:27)

3.   Green represents reptilian DNA, their present 'stage' color, while we, as humans have evolved through that stage and are about to move onto the last stage in this time frame, the ultra violet range.

Chapter 12

Interdemensional Physics

PYTHAGORAS

Pythagoras held three major doctrines:

1. Harmony of the Spheres

2. Doctrine of Numbers

3. Transmigration of Souls

In this chapter we will attempt to summarize the essence of the above three doctrines. Wherever possible, we will employ visual aides, most of which were computer-generated, either through AutoCAD or 3-D modeling programs.

To date we have only basically established the star alignments as they relate to the north and east faces of the Great Pyramid (Khufu). We will now explain how the south and west faces complete the overall model. As we already know, two of the four faces of the Great Pyramid are slightly longer than their opposite counterparts. (Others have already indicated and proven that two sides are made to the Pi proportion and the other two to the Phi proportion.) We must also consider that the Great Pyramid itself is not constructed in a straight line, that is, corner to corner. From each corner, the sides are slightly angled towards the center. This served the same purpose as the casing stone (fully explained in the previous chapter) to bring about, and incorporate, the difference of a 50-degree arc spread versus a 51.42857 degree arc spread.

In addition, we previously demonstrated how the plateau model was raised so that the Valley Temple of Khufu represented the northeast corner of the Great Pyramid (Pi proportion). We also demonstrated that the entrance to the

Hidden Room was set at precisely 30 degrees upward from that point. We now find that a 50-degree arc spread from that location elevated from that same location intersects the same point at precisely 25 degrees (midpoint).

When these same angles are repeated, from the identical southwest corner reference point, we find that there is a gap between the two mirrored end points. This is because we are dealing with a model that is directly proportional to the earth's relationship to these mirrored corners. Had we been working with the Mars (set) we would have found that these two points would have intersected if we had factored in the casing stone of Khafre. We know that the casing stone was applied to factor in the value of "0" (zero), and within our solar system, this zero point equals the exact location of our asteroid belt.

We now offer an overview of a few numbers that were provided to us in the Book of Genesis, 300, 50 and 30.

GIZA PLATEAU AND THE YEAR 2012

Points to Consider:
1. The Great Pyramid of Khufu (Cheops) is offset true north by 24 feet, or 3.7142 degrees.
2. The angle of separation lying between the valley temple of Khufu and the Sphinx temple is set at 3.714 degrees.
3. Two sides of the Great Pyramid are laid out to the value of Pi (22/7) calculated as 3.142857142857 etc.,and two sides laid out to Phi, the Golden or Divine ratio, that is mathematically half the square root of 5 plus 1 = 1.618034.

THE GENESIS CONNECTION

The critical recurring number set here is 7142857. Remember, the degrees true north the Great Pyramid is offset are 3.714285.If one were to place these numbers in a vertical row in a series of 7 (God created heaven and earth in 6 days; on the 7th day he rested) keeping the figure 7 in alignment, the result would be thus:

        7142857
        5714285
        8571428
        2857142
        4285714
        1428571
        7142857

If these numbers were aligned to 30 degrees, you would have the 12 houses (the Zodiac) — in other words, the trajectories of each set, at the time of growth. By advancing forward one unit each in its own set, this set creates changes to the other 12 houses.

These "lineage" sets are millions per galaxy, and determine and identify the exact stage each body is in relationship to the process at any given time. It also gives the location of all six sources of relative energy input. That is, God created the heavens and earth in 6 days, etc. Three of the six points are in negative displacement, and the other three are in positive form. This is tetrahedron geometry. This alignment, therefore, controls our orbital spin and tilt, etc.

As the universe expands, spatial relationships must also move forward; the decimal side numbers, 3,6,9 are non-existent. This set is repetitive and infinite, and if they did not exist, this would create an opportunity for the chaos model to exist.

This is where the figure 7 comes in, such as in the relation to star clusters, Pleiades, Alcor, Maser, etc. It is possible that these could be the capstones on a completed set, and at that point, become a cornerstone of the next set.

Here is an example of how we could work out our place in the universe utilizing the Great Pyramid. Again, using figures as mentioned in Genesis and descriptions in Exodus, we will explore the possibilities.

Noah's Ark:

> Length 300 cubits (degrees)
> Width 50 cubits (degrees)
> Max height 30 cubits (degrees)

To find value of zero: The width is fixed in the system at 50 degrees, so each lineage is set to a maximum of a 50-degree arc spread. Each lineage is angled in at 30 degrees, as per pyramid model.

"God created Heavens" in 6 days = 6 x 50 = 300

"On the Seventh Day He rested" = 7 x 50 = 350

360 - 350 = 10 degrees

10/7 = 1.42857 degrees.

So the value of '0' = 1.42857 degrees.

Another way is to say the spatial relation = 360/7 = 51.428571

Width = 50 degrees.

Value of 0 = 1.4285714, or 10/7.

The Great Pyramid is offset true North (24 feet), or in degrees, 3.7142857.

3.7142857 / 2 = 1.8571428 + value of 1.

1.8571428
1 + 1 = 19.571428

Therefore, from the above, the conclusions below may be summarized:

1. On December 21, 2012, the Plateau and the universe from the center when the value of zero is factored, will be in complete alignment.

2. The Giza Plateau sits on the only spot on Earth where the planet could accurately reveal this complex set.e stars in a set as the 2012 time approaches, or the Helix nearing alignment.

The stars in a set as the 2012 time approaches, or the Helix nearing alignment:
This alignment is in our linear lineage, where the 12 houses of the center sphere's origin are aligning.

We will now introduce an Auto-Cad model (2-D). It is hoped that this will explain the precision with which our controlled universe expansion system works.

Figure 12.1 — Autocad Model No.1

In this model we find that, like our pyramid data, the outside triangles are moving forward at a precise 30-degree angle, in an upward direction, whereas the center triangle is advancing straight down (up) the center line. The pyramid, or triangle found at the center bottom of these stacked pyramids, represents our Sun. The center or focus point of each pyramid in our model is located at the center bottom (base) of each of the pyramids. This was demonstrated on our pyramid plateau overall layout, which in fact marks the location of the "yet" to be opened Hall of Records (HOR). As this point represents dead center of the object, its overall influence on its related counterpart (to its outside) is factored in at 1.42857 degrees; explained fully in previous chapters.

As we stated in one of the earlier chapters, each time total alignment occurs, all objects will advance to the next stage in their own given linear directions; and as they are moving in various 30-degree relationships, they will continue to advance until they equal the object whose existence they help substantiate.

Figure 12.2 —— Autocad Model No.2

Although we used a two-dimensional model, one can visualize that over time this directional movement can be observed to be (overall) creating a half-helix effect. Because of the nature of the system, eventually we reach the point where maximum alignment (in positive/negative fields) occurs. This alignment would be considered as bordering on zero-degree alignment (relative), at which point the object in question remains and exists, until the next alignment is to occur. In addition, because the objects (in this case, stars) once again will advance in their own given direction of outward forward motion, they must then be viewed as having a negative influence on said object.

All physical (and non-physical) objects within our universe work according to this very simple growth model, whether we look at sub-atomic particles (or below) or on the Galactic scale. But for the time being, for the purposes of this chapter, we will show you how this system controls our own Solar System.

On December 21, 2012, at precisely 18 minutes and 13 seconds past 10:00 p.m. local Cairo time, our present time frame will come to an end, and all matter will advance to its next state of existence. A new time frame will also begin.

The above data is shown to us on the plateau model, and reinforced by the Mayan astrological calculations, one having been made to the Pi proportion, and the other to the Phi proportion. The data that we have deciphered from the above sources and added to our interpretation of Genesis, Exodus and Revelation indicate that the following series of changes within our Solar System will occur simultaneously.

A new star "X" and a new star "Y" will enter into our model, and as they advance, so too will our Sun, along with all other bodies. This advancement will pick up and lock in the new planet, which will now be controlled under the 30, 50, 300-degree criteria, as was the planet that preceded it during the last alignment. One must bear in mind that all bodies are moving simultaneously, as Mercury, Venus, Earth, Mars, etc., move to their next level.

This newly formed planet will evolve in the same fashion as all planets that preceded it. As motion creates energy, over time this new planet will begin to form its own energy through internal alignments, and a core will be established. The maximum extent of the core (size) will be proportional to the extent of the influence stars "X" and "Y" exert on it at that distance.

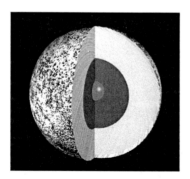

Figure 12.3 — Planet Mercury—Inner Core

To make it easier to understand, a series of diagrams have been created and we strongly suggest that one absorb these images for clarification. We have also included a few crop circle pictures that were provided by Lucy Pringle (a well-known crop circle researcher) to offer a visual aid during this period of discovery. However, we must remember that these images are 2-D; whereas we were able to create ours in 3-D.

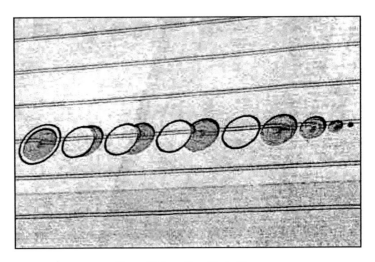

Figure 12.4 — Crop Circle Rings

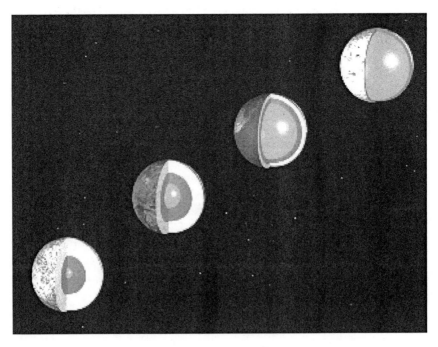

Figure 12.5 — The Inner Planets

Figure 12.6 —— The Inner Rings on the Planets

Figure 12.7 —— Crop Circle

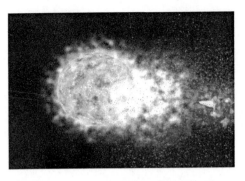

Figure 12.8 — Sun Giving Birth to Our New Planet

In this diagram above we see the birth of our new planet. Adam is our Sun and our new Planet Eve, created from his side (rib) will then become a living Cain/Abel, etc.

It is now important to explain how the orbital plane of the planets is determined and maintained.

The inner planets are mostly under the influence and controlled from the Pi side, which consists of six stars: first, our Sun, as well as the star that preceded it in this direct lineage, as well as star "X" and the star that preceded it in its linear lineage, as is star "Y," and that star that preceded it; and so on. Each of these six astral bodies is a star that forms part of six of the 12 houses of the Zodiac.

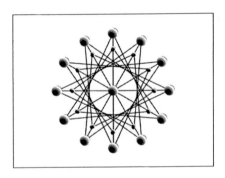

Figure 12.9 — The 12 Houses

Now the Phi side comprises a star and its predecessor in the same pattern as the Pi side, except that the angle and direction of these six stars are coming in at opposite 30-degree angles, each having a maximum area of control equal to a 50-degree arc spread. These six stars are individually located in the other six of the 12 houses. The distance of the "0" space between the Pi and Phi systems (as it relates to the inner planets) accounts for the elliptical orbits.

In the first diagram (*prior page, figure 12.9*) we show the 12 houses with a fixed center point and have drawn in and marked the required 50-degree maximum arc spread. In the second diagram, we have put in the same 50-degree arc spread extending from each of the stars (one in each of the 12 houses).

The third diagram shows the 30-degree angle of the six houses on the Pi side and the opposite 30-degree angle as seen from the Phi side. In this third picture, it is in this "trough" that is created, that the orbit of the inner body in question is determined and consequently set.

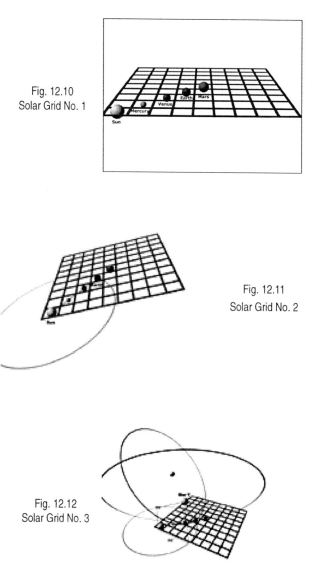

Fig. 12.10
Solar Grid No. 1

Fig. 12.11
Solar Grid No. 2

Fig. 12.12
Solar Grid No. 3

The next series of pictures, in 3-dimensional form, walk us through the exact locations and angles of the 12 stars, one in each of the 12 houses of the Zodiac. All of the stars are set precisely as they will appear in the sky relative to the December 21, 2012 alignment.

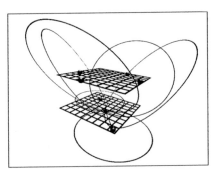

Figure 12.13
Solar Grid No. 4

All of the diagrams are set to the 30-degree angle and to a 50-degree arc spread. Six of the stars are set in grids that are angled up, and stacked in layers in similar manner to the pyramid and coming from the Pi side.

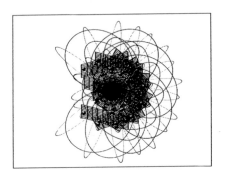

Figure 12.14
Solar Grid No. 5

In the last picture, the remaining six, also shown in grid form, are coming in from the opposite direction (also a form of layering).

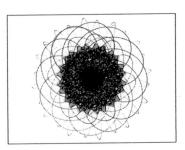

Figure 12.15
Final Grid

In the following two diagrams, we have incorporated the drawing of the 12 houses of the individual stars that make up our 12 houses. You can see that it becomes a very congested picture. We then remove the grids from the picture and begin to look at the end results from various camera angles.

The first of the three pictures below is the camera angle from the top view of our model. Notice the Helix that has formed; the blue sphere in the center of the model represents the Earth. It is also interesting here to note the form of the Egyptian Merkaba.

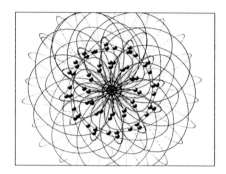

Figure 12.16
The 12 Houses A

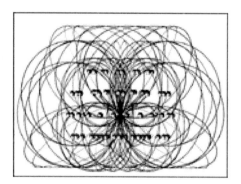

Fig. 12.17
The 12 Houses B

Fig. 12.18
The 12 Houses C

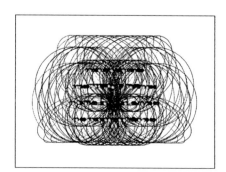

In Genesis, the 12 tribes of Israel relate to the 12 Individual Stars, of which one star is located in each of the 12 Houses of the Zodiac. In the book of Revelation, and described in the "New Creation" chapter, we find that when the alignment is in place, each of the 12 Tribes is aligned to its 12 Tribes (Angels). As a result of this alignment, the Earth itself exists. The total number of stars that justifies its existence in this time and space is: (12 x 12) +12 = 156.

The Pyramid of Khufu consists of 153 courses of stone from the base to the uncapped top. If we were to add to the 153 the equivalent value of three-dimensional "0"(3.142857) we find that the result is 153+3.142857 = 156 PLUS the value of "0"(1.42857).

Many angles of our 3D model provided us with imagery to which we could associate many items directly. However, we will terminate this particular chapter with a few of these images on which to ponder. In the meantime, the first picture is a side view of the model. Adjacent to it is a picture of a recent crop circle. Bear in mind that they are drawing out these crop circles in two dimensions, whereas our model is three-dimensional.

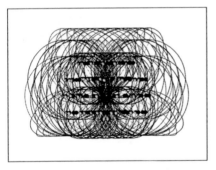

Figure 12.19 — The House and Stars

Fig. 12.20 — Crop Circle

The next picture is a top view angle, once more. This picture is where we calculated the locations of the 144 stars of each of the other inner planets, that is, Mercury and Venus, in addition to Mars.

Figure 12.21
The 144 Stars

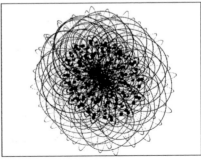

This demonstrates to us something unique; that this alignment is responsible for creating one-third of our 12-strand D.N.A.

The final sting in the tail.

Previously, we illustrated the final decipherment of the overall Plateau Model. At this juncture, we will demonstrate how to read it and what it means. This may seem rather obvious, now that it has been worked out.

This model offers the alignment from the Plateau as it occurred on May 5, 2000, when the three Pyramids were inserted into the model where the location of the Pyramid Kaphre is situated (as it is with its placement on the physical layout in relation to the other two pyramids).

It does so in the following manner:

From atop the Pyramid we call Horus, or Isis, we notice that it is precisely 15 degrees offset from the location of the Hall of Records to where the outside corner of Khefre (which represents the planet Mars) meets the model's baseline. As the Hall of Records is placed in a location to reflect the location of the center of Planet Earth, we have used this location point from which we calculated the exact time of day in which the alignment occurred on May 5, 2000.

From the location of the Hall of Records (at the precise time of alignment) Mars was exactly 15 degrees offset at the time the alignment occurred. *(See picture below.)*

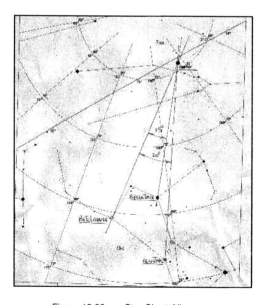

Figure 12.22 — Star Chart Alignment

Chapter 13

Drawings - The Analysis

Although the information contained in this section is the result of lengthy research by the authors, it is nonetheless always an added bonus when such information appears to confirm one's findings, no matter how trivial these discoveries may seem. Such was the case recently while we were investigating this particular segment of our research, where a few pages of drawings and representative "glyphs" (similar in appearance to Egyptian and Mayan hieroglyphs) came into our possession for commentary analysis. Not only did these representations confirm our existing theses; they also offered additional insights as to what occurred on the Giza Plateau on May 5, and what may subsequently occur before or on December 21, 2012.

A person who, as far as we can ascertain, held no prior knowledge, history or understanding of the layout of the Giza complex, drew the sketches. The information came to the individual via a "paranormal" route, that is, something that cannot be explained rationally, and possibly involved an alien abduction scenario. A British research organization specializing in such matters conducted the original investigation. Thus, for obvious reasons of security, anonymity and ongoing case investigation procedures, we are obliged not to release the individual's name.

The individual received the drawings in what seemed to be a jumble of collected words, numbers, glyphs and shapes, often appearing to be an unrelated scrabble of unknown representations. However, upon serious analysis by our experienced team, we discovered that not only were the drawings highly relevant and crucial to the understanding of the layout of the Giza complex, but the work seemed to originate from a source with highly advanced scientific knowledge – i.e., knowledge of astrophysics, mathematics and astronomy, etc.

Since these representations confirmed our own findings, we considered it crucial to include an analysis in this chapter. In essence, they assist in the understanding towards what occurred, or will occur, in relation to the Plateau on May 5, 2000, and on December 21, 2012.

THE "DRAWINGS" DECODED

The center focus of this first diagram is the upright marker, which appears to have three upper markers and one much farther down located at its base. The upper markings are pointing, one to the left, the second to the right and the other, toward the center. We believe these markings are oriented toward the three pyramids located on the plateau: Khufu, Khaphre and Menkaure. This marker appears to be located on or near the causeway heading towards the Pyramid of Khaphre. This is apparent when one studies the multi-leveled diagram above it. Later we will discuss further explanation on the upper part of the drawing. For now, we will be looking at the objects lying around the marker. *Note that we use the marker as the main point of reference.*

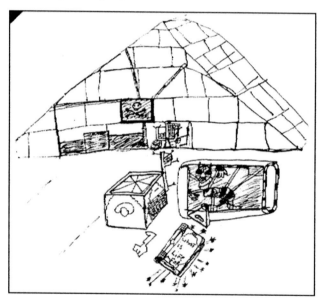

Figure 13.1 - Plateau drawing - Decipher No.1

The box located immediately to the left of the marker (our center line) is covered with symbolism. On the front face it indicates a hole (small circle) lying on the edge of a larger hole, and the perceptual location appears to be that of a roadway, or in this case, a causeway. A stepped niche appears to be located on the right-hand side of this box, similar to the one located in the Queen's Chamber inside the pyramid of Khufu. The entrance on the side of the box is represented by the presence of the grill. On the top of this box appears a set of intersecting lines, each offset 45 degrees to the next. This is interpreted to mean that the box, and, or its interior (or something inside the box) is precisely aligned to some exterior criteria, as yet unknown

The top of the box appears to be open. Judging by the thickness of the walls of the box, it was relatively straightforward to ascertain that this was indeed meant as a coffer or sarcophagus. The sarcophagus located inside the King's Chamber is also without a top. Also, it is offset to the left of the meridian of the Pyramid itself. It appears self-evident that this box represents the location of the Tomb of Osiris, in addition to the contents of that tomb. Remember, inside the tomb itself they have only discovered the sarcophagus with four pillars, one located at each corner. These are the markers from which the unknown exterior markings will, when aligned, give the precise location of the sarcophagus itself.

The entrance to this Tomb was indeed accessed from under the causeway leading to Kaphre. In addition, it is important to note that the Tomb itself is offset.

Figure 13.2 - Plateau Drawing - Decipher No. 2

The next element of the drawing is the fork-like symbol lying next to the box. This marker lies at an angle to the box (The Tomb of Osiris) also to the right of the marker. It has two offsets in its handle, one to the left and one to the right, indicating that it is located at its endpoint to the right of the tomb, in addition to being at a shifted angle from the center marker. This forked marker is pointed at the blocked end of what appears to be a tunnel or chamber, the front of the fork pointing to the east, toward the location of the Hall of Records.

The book is also found to be lying at an angle similar to that of the key, only proportionally farther over. On it is written, "what is life for." The symbolism of the book, along with the title and Stars shown to be moving in a linear motion, were interpreted to be the Hall of Records. This conclusion is made with the knowledge gained from the second drawing, which will now be explained in greater detail. The only additional element found in this cluster is that of a small pyramid, which we noticed is at the same angle at which the book is pointing. Within this Pyramid there appears to be a mummy, inside or beneath its center point. We believe this pyramid is meant to represent the pyramid Horus. The location of the Hall of Records would appear to be the point from where the angles are drawn out, to identify the locations of both a chamber housing some live non-human being, or beings, and a further location where a mummy, or a body, is buried beneath a pyramid. The upper part of the diagram, as previously stated, is multi-layered.

First, we observe a chamber, which appears to house only a single sarcophagus. Beside this (on the right-hand side) we observe a door ajar, and whatever was inside has spilt out onto the Plateau. We trust that the Skull and Crossbones Box, between the two, is not inserted to represent the groups who will be responsible for the opening of the Tomb of Osiris. Two shafts lead down into the same box, and we have been informed that the Association for Research and Enlightenment (A.R.E) and the National Geographic Organization will be funding an expedition, along with additional private financial backing, in an attempt to open this tomb. One would think that A.R.E. would have at least heeded the spoken words of Edgar Cayce.

Edgar Cayce was born on a farm near Hopkinsville, Kentucky. At the age of twenty-one he developed a gradual throat paralysis which threatened the loss of his voice. Doctors were unable to find a cause for his condition. Cayce used to enter into the same hypnotic sleep that had enabled him to learn his school lessons some years before, and while in that state, he was able to recommend a cure that successfully repaired his throat muscles and restored his voice. It was soon discovered that he could do the same for others.

For most of his adult life, Cayce was able to provide intuitive insights into many diverse questions. When he was in a self-induced sleep state, he could respond to any question asked of him. These responses became known as "readings." Initially, the information dealt mainly with medical problems. However, the scope of his readings expanded to include such topics as meditation, reincarnation and prophecy. Cayce eventually gave over 14,000 readings on more than 10,000 different topics to people all over the world. Reseachers continue to collect and write about this information.

Founded in 1931, The Association for Research and Enlightenment (A.R.E.), Inc., is the international headquarters of the work of Edgar Cayce, and its purpose is to preserve, research, and make available insights from Cayce's information.

The ARE states:

> *Upon the creation of the Foundation, the Edgar Cayce readings and their supporting documentation became the sole property of the Edgar Cayce Foundation. The Foundation provides permanent legal and physical custody of not only the readings and Edgar Cayce's correspondence, but also a variety of other historical records.*

Should they proceed as planned, we give this expedition ...

"THE FIRST WARNING"

The central focal point on the second diagram is in the corner, displaying a picture that depicts a dimensional time-slip mix. This segment of the picture (the spheres) represents specific criteria concerning a specific star alignment that would, when in place, create or produce the opportunity for a stargate or vortex to form. This stargate, or vortex, will extend outward in the direction from which it is being pointed to, by the arrow-like marker, drawn down by its lower end. In addition to establishing a direction, we find drawn in, next to the vertical dimension mix line, a picture of what appears to be a vertical shaft holding six horizontal segments.

It must be noted that the six horizontal segments are not held apart by any noticeable segments. This is in comparison to the two sets of three horizontal segments shown separated in the same type of drawing located at the top of the page, where we notice between the two sets, a drawn-in segment of the vertical shaft.

We have identified the objects in this main diagram segment as a star alignment. On the diagram itself there are no indications as to their identities. Through our own research, however, we have been able to recognize not only the identity of these astral bodies, but the time at which this alignment will occur (discussed in the "Star Alignment" section). In the next part of the drawing we looked at the row of five triangles, with four inverted triangles inserted between the original five. This was interpreted as the representation that when two like sources intersect, a vortex is created, and through this realignment a stargate is formed. Comparing the satellite images of the stargates emanating from the sun with this triangular model, it appears that the inner spiral of those stargates demonstrates a similar observation if one were to loop through the use of a continuous line between these triangles (or pyramids). In the next item, we discover for the second time a two-pronged marker.

Could this marker be indicating the convergence, from two separate points of origin intersecting at a specific point and moving forward on the directional path of the primary one? To us this seemed to be consistent with the dimensional mix line as well as the main aligned body of spheres; thus producing the opportunity for a time slide to occur.

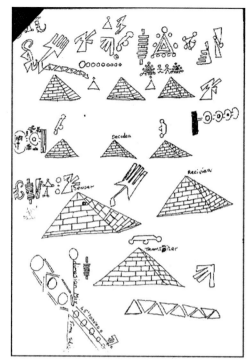

Figure 13.3 - Plateau Drawing - Decipher No. 3

Now we will look to the main body of the picture (or drawing) that consists of eleven pyramid structures, nine of which are very much straightforward-looking pyramids. The other two appear as open triangles, each with a sphere centered immediately above each apex. These spheres are definitely placed to represent stars, thus indicating placement as a result of star alignment. The placement of the triangles themselves is of note also, since they appear to be among the three pyramids located below them.

If we were to take the obvious into account, we could then interpret this as meaning that, viewed from the Plateau, when a star alignment (a specific star alignment) would occur and if a stargate were to form, its end point would be the plateau. We now come to the analysis of the four pyramids that are individually labeled as "Transmitter," "Sender," "Decoder" and "Receiver." The one marked as Transmitter has a unique symbol above it. This symbol is in a horizontal position, whereas the similar type of symbols appearing over two of the other end pyramids (of a three-pyramid set) are at facing angles. If we were to take these two symbols that are facing each other and superimpose them together, using the spheres as the focal point, we would discover that this same imagery appears in the dimensional mix diagram. We are actually seeing that the main directional flow has alternatively been re-routed around the center sphere.

Returning to the Transmitter pyramid, one would interpret that the energy transmitted to the Receiver pyramid is being re-routed through the Sender pyramid. Thus, even though redirected, it still arrives at the intended receiver then to be decoded; in other words, taken back to its original state. The four-pronged fork-like marker is now taken into account. This marker is pointing in the direction of the set of three pyramids. However, it is angled and not pointing directly at any of the pyramids themselves. Note that the handle in its offset position is pointing down toward the Sender pyramid.

Recalling the first picture that was previously interpreted, there appeared a three- pronged fork-type marker also, which was used as a directional aid and placed at an angle in a direction away from the Pyramids.

The three-pronged fork fits into the spaces of the four-pronged fork, thus filling in the gaps and producing a whole complete unit. Having tied the two pictures together, we have now traced the flow from the source, i.e., from the Transmitter pyramid, and we have been able to place its endpoint onto the plateau.

More precisely, by interpreting the two pictures, we have been able to fix its endpoint on or near the location of Tomb No 2. Thus, the connection is made.

Additional markings contained in the drawing, support the premise that someone, or something, at the time the portal will open, will utilize this stargate in order to relocate to the plateau.

Observe the two sets of triangles, a larger triangle with two smaller inset triangles, each having the same outer spheres located around both. This is placed to

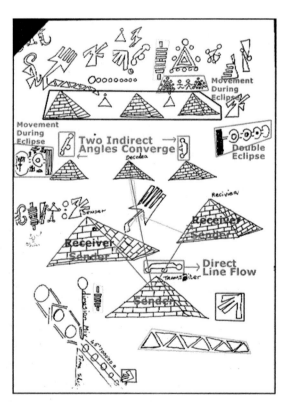

Figure 13.4 - Plateau DrawingDecipher No. 4

point out that in this three-dimensional reality when this star alignment occurs, it creates a passageway making it possible to travel between the two points. Also, notice the two stickmen, one of which is in ready stance, while the other is shown rushing toward the other pyramid set. In addition, we observe the string of nine spheres. This could indicate that this is an event that will occur within our own nine-planet solar system. Also shown is the rather obvious representation of a flow of spheres where an eclipse-like event is occurring, culminating in its fourth space, which is void. Could this mean that

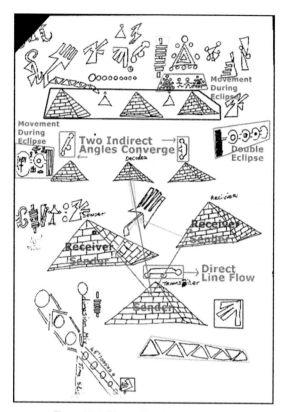

Figure 13.5 - Plateau Drawing - Decipher No. 5

the non-human beings beneath the plateau, presently awakening and in a confined space, would have to be released in order to activate equipment — probably located somewhere beneath the Plateau — in order to establish an end point for someone or something to target? We believe this to be the case! It is apparent that there is a deflected energy source coming in at an angle, which, when it intersects with a direct flow, creates a spiraling effect; in turn, creating a stargate. The up-side to all of this is the fact one possesses the knowledge that these stargates are dependent on energy (directional) flow. It would then be possible, if one were able to re-route the energy flow, that one could then control its endpoint. Or, put another way, one could re-direct the location where the portal (or endpoint) of the stargate would be opening up. Aeons ago, someone in the history of this planet possessed the understanding and ability, not to mention the foresight, to position just such a defense system. We refer to this defense system as the "Shield." This shield is controlled by a series of strategically placed "crystals," all of which are located deep beneath the surface on points which we often refer to as the key points marking what we call the Cathie Grid.[1]

This entire global grid is controlled by one very complex crystal grouping, and it is this grouping that we refer to as The Crystal. *(See Chapter 11, "The Great Experiment.")*

The primary location of this Crystal is beneath the central power point, deep beneath the Plateau. Even though the non-human beings would like to decommission this out of service, they cannot approach it. Only one individual known by various names can accomplish this task. However, we will refer to the name given to him in the book of Genesis: **Joseph.**

Joseph rests in a coffin (sarcophagus) close to where The Crystal is stored. He lies in wait,

Figure 13.6 Solar Stargate

deep beneath the plateau, below the pyramid we have referred to as Horus (the southernmost Queen's Pyramid of Khufu). This tomb is only accessible through the entrance leading down from the floor in the hidden room accessed off the Grand Gallery, as detailed in our previous chapter. Unlike the non-human beings now awakening, he must wait to be awakened.

A genetic key is required to awaken him from his state of suspended animation, in order to bring him back to life. This genetic key has been passed down from generation to generation, through the descendants of Abraham. But time is running out, and Jacob's older brother, Esau, will do all he can to block Joseph's awakening.

The Giza Plateau Alignment - May 5th 2000:
The Stargate.

The following data was calculated where one would observe the heavens above the Giza Plateau, Egypt, at co-ordinates 29 degrees 58' 29" N 31 degrees 8' 28" at 10.00 hours (or 08.00 Zulu time) local time Cairo, on May 5th 2000.

Software used was "Cybersky" and independently confirmed by utilizing Sky Map pro 6 and Gray Stel Star Atlas 3.

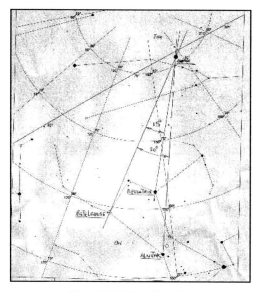

Figure 13.17 - Star Chart A

On May 5, 2000, Planet Earth witnessed what many call the "Grand Alignment." Although not a rare event in the history of this planet, it is nonetheless an unusual alignment of the Sun, Moon, and the planets Mercury, Venus, Mars, Jupiter and Saturn. This occurs within the same area of the sky, spread over a 25 degrees 53 minutes arc, where our sun is at the center of this massing. However, and more important, a line may be drawn through the sun, Jupiter and Saturn directly to Betelgeuse, the main star in the constellation of Orion.From the three stars in Orion's belt, Alnitak, Alnilam and Mintaka, an additional line may be drawn across to intersect with the planet Mars; thus, in essence constructing the formation of our "Stargate."

THE 'PHYSICS'

Recently, we have been witnessing increasing solar flare and Coronal Mass Ejection activity (CME's) from our sun, due, as some would have us believe, to the peak 11-year "Solar Cycle," arriving at its maximum in April, 2000. The first of these solar occurrences this year occurred on February 17, when a medium solar-sized flare erupted from the sun accompanied by a CME.[2] NASA admitted this was an unexpected event, since it originated where little previous activity had occurred. Surprise, surprise! On February 23, M class flares continued for six consecutive days. No previous record of three similar flares have been recorded, let alone six! Finally, on February 24, NASA sent out an alert, stating that a substantial magnetic storm may be heading this way. However, there was no mention of the seven continuous days of M class solar flares. In addition, the BBC Internet New Sci-Tech page produced an article on February 7, "Major Flare Erupts on Sun."

In essence, in mid-April earlier in the year, the maximum solar flare and associated high electromagnetic activity was observed for some time. In conjunction with this activity, one associates related failures in orbiting satellites, communication failures and other electrical problems. In short, it was expected that a number of electrical problems and shut-downs due to the increase, would result from the bombardment of these flares on our atmosphere.

What does all this mean, and what is the relation to the Giza Plateau? On the basis of our original work, and what we have stated concerning the Giza-Genesis connection, we may take this at least one stage further toward arriving at an understanding of what occurred on the Giza Plateau on May 5, 2000. Initially we pointed out that the earth was conceived by two sets of lineage. The first is our solar sun and the second is the mathematical set of the six identified in the Bible as Adam, Seth, Enosh, Cainan (Kenan), Mahalaleel and Jared. Adam is the point of origin in our "star map" — zero degrees. For example, Adam (Terah) is Alcyone in the Pleiades; Abram, our sun; and Abraham, planet Earth.

On May 5, 2000, as mentioned above, "The Grand Alignment" occurred. But what does this mean in relation to the Giza Plateau complex?

Plenty!

At 10:00 o'clock, local time Cairo, our sun was in direct line with Jupiter and Saturn. Using our Genesis thesis, we equate Jupiter with Japheth and Saturn with Shem (with Ham were the three sons of Noah). Thus, one is able to draw a line through the middle of these heavenly bodies that ultimately runs through the star of Betelgeuse in the constellation of Orion. Betelgeuse is related to the Plateau as the star of Bethlehem (Betel).

The influence of Betelgeuse on our sun is now temporarily interrupted due to the positioning of Saturn and Jupiter. In addition, also at that exact time, the three belt stars of Orion, Alnitak, Alnilam and Mintake were in direct line with Mars. In other words, one is able to draw a straight line through these three stars running parallel through the planet Mars! Because of the star's influence at that time, the energy flow was redirectedfrom the planet Mars at the exact time of the Betelgeuse - Saturn - Jupiter angular alignment. This calculated to be approximately 30 degrees.

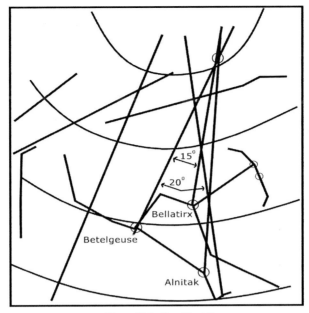

Figure 13.8 - Star Chart B

MARS EENERGY FLOW

There has been much speculation over recent years on the relation to an area on Mars known as Cydonia,[3] where structures such as "The Face" and pyramids similar to the ones located at Giza, have been discovered. One of the pyramidal structures seems to demonstrate a five-sided pyramid, known as the D and M Pyramid of Mars.[4]

We believe that this five-sided pyramidal structure is the focal point for the redirection of energy flow at the stipulated time of the alignment; in essence, assisting towards the "release" of the Stargate, culminating in a vortex opening.

Notes

1.   Bruce Cathie and the "Global Grid". The modern scientific history of the Global Grid could be said to have begun with the work of a researcher named Bruce Cathie. Cathie writes on highly complicated mathematical ideas as if they were as simple as school arithmetic.

In pursuit of more intensive research, Cathie was led to French researcher Aime Michel, who had been studying UFOs for many years and had determined some of the standard flight paths that they would follow in various parts of Europe. UFO sightings would occur time and time again along these tracklines and Michel determined that the average distance between these lines was 54.46 kilometers. When converting this over to nautical miles, Cathie discovered to his own surprise that the tracklines were **exactly 30 nautical miles apart.** Again, 30 is a fundamental "harmonic" or frequency number.

Cathie found that the lines of magnetic force that made up the Global Grid are always 30 arc-minutes apart. If this is correct the adaptation of 360 degrees to a planetary sphere may simply be an observation of the organization of its lines of force. Thus, from Cathie's discoveries, we know that every half-degree of arc on the Earth's surface was a potential UFO trackline, for a total of 720 latitude lines and 720 longitude lines.

> *I found that by using units of 30 minutes of arc latitude north-south, and 30 minutes of arc longitude east-west, on my Mercator's map, a grid pattern was formed into which a great number of UFO reports could be fitted. I eventually had a map with sixteen stationary and seventeen moving UFOs plotted on grid intersections and tracklines.*
>
> *Having satisfied myself that my reasoning and plotting were not false, I consider that I had good proof that New Zealand, possibly other countries, and probably the whole world, were being systematically covered by some type of grid system.*
>
> — Captain Bruce Cathie

2.   "Here Comes the Sun"

> *A solar flare on February 17 was accompanied by a coronal mass ejection that appears to be almost directly be headed almost directly for Earth. Geomagnetic activity, including aurora, may be observed beginning February 19th or 20th.*
> — NASA *Space Science News,* February 18th 2000
> February 18, 2000 — *Yesterday, a medium-sized solar flare erupted from a sunspot group near the middle of the solar disk. It was accompanied by a Coronal Mass Ejection CME that appears to be headed directly for our planet. There's no cause for alarm — CMEs aren't dangerous to people — but this one could trigger beautiful aurorae and other geomagnetic activity when it passes by our planet around February 20.*
>
> *Two M-class solar flares erupted in quick succession on February 17. Both events were somewhat unexpected as the sunspot groups they came from showed very little activity prior to flaring. The second flare, in particular, occurred near a small and apparently innocuous sunspot identified by the NOAA Space Environment Center as active region # 8872. The eruption from 8872 was accompanied by a coronal "halo event." Halo events are coronal mass ejections aimed toward the Earth. As they loom larger and larger they appear to envelope the Sun, forming a halo around our star.*
> *Coronal mass ejections can carry up to 10 billion tons of plasma traveling at speeds as high as 2000 km/s. When they collide directly with Earth they can excite geomagnetic storms, which have been linked to satellite communication failures. In extreme cases, such storms can induce electric currents in the Earth and oceans that interfere with or even damage electric power transmission equipment. Energetic particles and radiation from solar flares reach the Earth in just minutes. The slower-moving material from a coronal mass ejection usually takes days to reach our planet. The leading edge*

of the February 17 CME could reach the Earth by February 19 or 20.
— From: http://www.spacescience.com/headlines/y2000/ast18feb_1.htm

3. An area on the surface of the planet Mars, known as Cydonia, seems to have a number of "anomalies" including a structure similar to a human looking face of large proportions. There are a number of structures nearby with various names, such as "Inca city."

The thousands of images captured by Mars Global Surveyor, have been subjected to scrutiny by many researchers, of which a summary of one report is included here.

Analysis of Global Surveyor Imagery of the Face on Mars.
New findings from Mars Global Surveyor sustain the hypothesis that the Face on Mars may be artificial

John Carlotto:
> *On April 5 1998, after over twenty years, the Mars Global Surveyor (MGS) re-imaged the Face on Mars. The Face is one of a number of anomalous objects on the surface of Mars though to be artificial in origin (DiPietro and Molenaar 1988, Hoagland 1992, McDaniel 1994, Carlotto 1997, McDaniel and Paxson 1998). Initially imaged by a Viking orbiter spacecraft in 1976, the impression of a face was striking. But close up MGS reveals the formation to be rough and highly eroded. Many have therefore concluded that the Face is natural. But others contend that if the Face is artificial it must certainly be very old and highly eroded. Thus the question remains as to how to distinguish an eroded artificial feature from a natural one (Brandenburg et al 1991). We believe that it is premature at this time to render any definitive judgment concerning a natural origin for the Face. Although the new image is insufficient to provide definitive proof for artificiality, there are many anomalous qualities to the Face on Mars that remain unexplained.*
> — http://www.psrw.com/~markc/Articles/MGSreport/paper.html

4. The "D and M pyramid" is a five-sided pyramid structure located in the "Cydonia" region on the surface of Mars.
> *In Viking imagery, the three illuminated faces of the D&M appear to be relatively flat with well-defined edges in between. Buttress-like structures at the base of several edges are also evident. In the MGS image the edge between the northeast and northwest faces resembles a spine running from the apex of the D&M down to the ground. At the base of the spine lies a circular depression, possibly an opening. A dark feature seems to emanate northward from this depression or opening, which then leads into a sinuous channel off to the right. What is this dark feature? A shadow within a deep trench seems unlikely, due to the lack of significant shadowing in the image. Another possibility is some kind of dark material flowing out of the D&M.*
> — *Cydonia Update* Mark Carlotto 1999

— http://www.psrw.com/~markc/Articles/cydoniaUpdate/index.html

Chapter 14

On the Eighth Day

THE CRYSTAL AND THE GLOBAL GRID ACTIVATION

Most of the following data has been collected from diverse sources, including government data (magnetometer and solar charts), weather and radar maps. Several individuals throughout the world have assisted in compiling this data. These dedicated persons also have played a key role in helping to erect the protective global grid, now in place around our ionosphere. We are grateful to them, fully acknowledging the tremendous effort and sacrifice involved in developing and securing this grid.

The information presented in this vitally important section is only a small part of a long and complex series of events, covering a diverse range of topics concerning our origins in the solar system and the cosmos. Since "time," as we presently comprehend it, plays a vital role here, we will be brief yet comprehensive, providing as much available verifiable information as possible. Also because of this time factor, we offer a considerable amount of related reference data, including Solar satellite images, seismometer data, radar and magnetometer readings. One should follow this data carefully in order to understand what is about to occur on this planet Earth, Terra.

Within the current time frame, our little "third rock from the sun" happens to be in the most sought-after location in the galaxy; a piece of prime real estate, if you will. This fact, combined with the forthcoming zero time set date of December 21, 2012, brings us to the very heart of the matter at hand.

"A WAR IS RAGING IN THE HEAVENS"

A conflict beyond the planet Jupiter began in February, 2000. At regular periods, those of you who follow the SOHO and LASCO solar satellite images, will have noticed our old friend, the "Sun Cruiser," or "Plasma Carrier," orbiting the sun. This anomaly is considered to be of Eridanean origin (in the constellation of Eridanus). For additional information, see Chapter 10, "The Erideans and the An-unnaki."

Figure 14.1 — SOHO Solar Image

Figure 14.2 — SOHO Anomaly Enlargement

Some may equate this war with a religious conflict, the fallen angels, or good versus evil. As we shall see, indeed, this may be the case, for as we approach this end time, it is the individual who will be given the opportunity to make this ascension. Those who exist in this dimensional level after the end time will be at the mercy of the mind controllers. These mind controllers are, in reality, "slave masters." This is a very complicated scenario and would require a whole book in itself to explain how it works.

At this point, if one were to ask what would be the nearest description of exactly what scenario is unfolding, it would be a mix of the three films:

- *The Prophecy*[1]
- *The Fifth Element*[2]
- *The Matrix*[3]

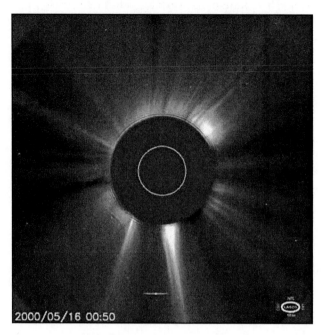

Figure 14.3 — Stargate

With that description, who wants to visit a cinema when the real event is unfolding before our very eyes! To cut a long and complex tale extremely short, and to put it bluntly, since May 5, 2000, alien races are "parked" out in the wings of our solar system waiting for an opportunity to enter an opening in our recently activated global grid. At present, this grid affords Earth the protection she needs.

However, there is one who has recently arisen from stasis below the Giza Plateau, who will ensure that this potential forced entry does not come to pass. This is a result of a pact made aeons ago, actually on the Giza Plateau itself.

It appears that an individual of a certain race may attempt to return to claim what he assumes to be his heritage. The May 5 event provided an ideal opportunity in which to carry this out via the stellar portal opening, or stargate, that occurred on that date.(*See stargate picture next page*)

The combined electromagnetic activity of the maximum solar radiation we are now experiencing would have assisted in this opportunity by damaging our global geomagnetic field, or grid that is normally present around our planet.

Thus, by replacing or strengthening this grid, the procedure of which will be dealt with later, the forced entry into our time frame will be diverted.

For a further understanding of the connection between these EM fields or grids, please refer to Chapter 11, "The Great Experiment." In that chapter, we explained the siting of crystals at what we term today "sacred sites," and the focal crystal that was placed below the Giza Plateau pyramid complex.

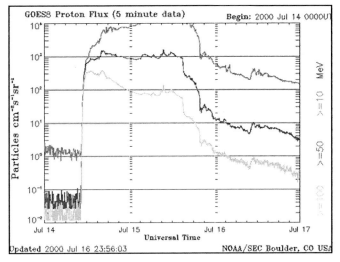

Figure 14.4 — Proton Flux Chart

In Appendix A, Julie King[4] explains the Red Grid and the Blue Grid. The Red Grid is manipulated by our military in conjunction with alien technology from the Zetas, who, for the most part, are now believed to have left this planet, prior to the "real" grid activation. The Blue Grid is the one that is now held in place to protect the planet, and continual work is in progress to maintain this protective grid.

It is now essential to follow the events that led up to May 5, including post, and continuing, effects.

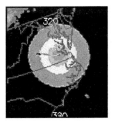

Figure 14.5 — Radar Ring[5]

BACKGROUND OF EVENTS TO PRESENT DAY

When "speed overrides security," it is essential to deliver the bare bones of what is occurring. Nostradamus called it the "The Three Waves," whereby the "First Wave" was a slow but sure and steady take-over of governing elite of this planet by an alien force. The "Second Wave" was the incoming and complete take-over by an alien race on this planet. The "Third Wave" was "Armageddon" itself. We may indeed be near the "Second Wave" scenario, whereby the grid held in place over this planet is the only protection we have.

Previously, we mentioned that three tombs are below the Plateau: Joseph, Elnil and Osiris. It is Joseph who is the "saving grace" in this present unfolding scenario.

In the early hours of May 5, the crystal was accessed and activated, thereby instigating the protective grid around the planet, assisted by numerous energy points interconnected around the globe at sacred sites. During this operation, Joseph awoke from stasis, as predestined to do so, while certain planetary events were experienced. It is from this point that we now explain the procedure and nature of this complex and delicate task.

In the days leading up to the alignment of May 5, 2000, several individuals (including groups of individuals) came together, physically and actually, at precisely the correct time. Each of these groups, or individuals, knew exactly what their "tasks" were and proceeded to execute what they had been trained to do. In other words, none of these persons was driven by any known motive other than belief. To simply say that all were successful would be a complete understatement. However, not all is over yet, so please bear this fact in mind as we attempt to relay the sequence of events as they unfolded in the hours leading up to the alignment.

This scenario is far from completed, and as there is much more at stake that can be imagined, the full complete details are yet to be analyzed. The alignment of May 5 was far more than a planetary alignment, since the true alignment concerned the Star of Betelguese in the Orion Constellation. This star is the Star of Bethlehem. In the book of Genesis we are consistently taken back to Betel, (the Star of Betelguese). But this is only part of the story. The second part concerns Ham, Noah's son, who would have left Noah in his nakedness, had it not been for his two brothers, who symbolically backed in and placed a coat over his nakedness, thus "cloaking" him. The two brothers are Shem (Star X), and Japeth (Star Y). (See Chapter 12 on "Interdimensional Physics.")

Once the whole Giza Pyramid "Complex" had been deciphered, we were then in a position to incorporate the knowledge contained in the Book of Genesis, providing the required tools from which to work. An additional and essential piece of information necessary to understand was that the Valley temple of Khufu represented the direct lineage (Adam) of our Sun.

In previous chapters, we explained how this Pyramid complex is constructed to specifically point out this alignment. This event occurs only once in every "cycle," where Betelguese aligns directly through our Sun to our planet Earth, or Terra.

In order to understand the scenario leading up to the May 5 event, including the continuing post-event effects, we consider it of utmost importance to present a detailed synopsis of the number of related planetary and associated events.

The information extracted and referenced from several sources, including military and government satellite images and data readings, has been taken directly from the source itself. There have been no alterations or additions other than enlargement of a few images for clarification, and all are available in their raw state. Basically, it is a case of WYSIWYG — What You See Is What You Get.

To comprehend the severity and importance surrounding the recent event, and to explain what will soon occur, it is essential to follow this data. On April 27, 2000, what can only be described as a "solar torpedo" was witnessed on the SOHO and LASCO solar satellite images, heading towards the sun.[6]

In addition, a similar event was witnessed in June, 1998.

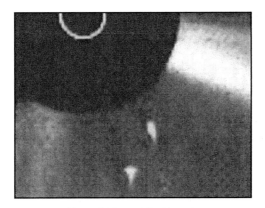

Figure 14.6 — Solar Torpedo

Before and during this event of April, a number of NASA image files appeared to be missing. For example, before this event, missing C3 files were: 20000428 and 20000429_0418. After the event, the missing files were: 20000430_0654 and 20000430_1054.

A complete analysis of this event was conducted.[7]

On the same day, April 30, massive Coronal Mass Ejections (CME's) were observed emanating from our sun, and witnessed by the SOHO and LASCO satellite images.

Figure 14.7
Solar Coronal
Mass Ejection (CME)

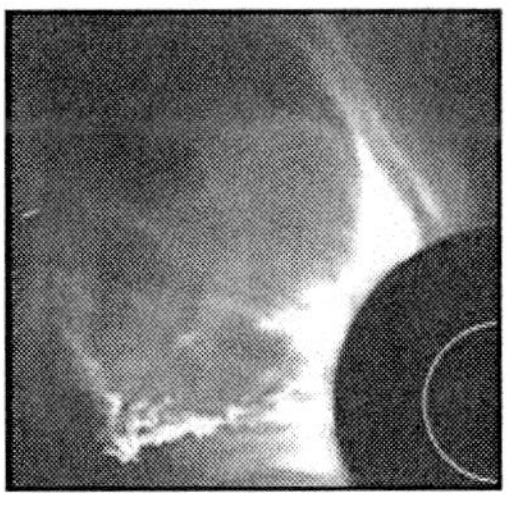

On May 1, 2000, we were scheduled to have our second interview with Jeff Rense on the highly acclaimed "Sightings" show. At that time, we were going to reveal certain aspects of the May 5 alignment that were connected with the Giza Plateau. However, the show was cancelled at the very last minute due to a "technical problem" totally out of Jeff's and the station's control. We did manage to get back on the show on May 8. Here is a summary of the transcript:

On May 4, 2000, an actual, physical planetary grid alignment took place under the pyramids at Giza. This was done to protect the earth and bring it into electromagnetic harmony. Rotating the plateau 120 degrees made it possible to locate the Bethlehem Processionway, which is the entrance to an area containing a machine that had to be activated in order for the alignment to occur.

A highly trained physical evidence acquisition team (PEA) physically and actually, entered the area, twice, from two different directions. The first time was to dismantle two "booby traps" to gain access to the room where the machine is housed. This involved "adjusting rocks on the walls." It had been rumored that teams that had tried to gain access before had encountered something of an explosive nature, resulting in the loss of lives. Therefore, it was necessary to disable these "booby traps" before accessing the room that houses the "machine."

After successfully dismantling the traps, the PEA team emerged to report what they had seen, and to receive instructions on how to operate the machine. When they went back in, they were challenged by the "guardians." They had to go through a complicated procedure answering questions as to who they were, why and for whom they were there, etc. When the "guardians" were satisfied, they "disappeared." The team then proceeded to the room where they found the "machine," which was running at the time.

The machine consisted of three parts. There was a central panel off to the side with three series of knobs. Three people had to man the knobs at the same time, in order for the machine to operate correctly. A disc had to be slid into a notch in the machine, parallel to the floor. Above was a mirror with parallel grooves running from the center. The machine is a crystal that is aimed directly at the pyramids.

The earth produces magnetic fields, and these were being changed. The crystals protect the earth and bring it into electromagnetic harmony. This machine is relevant and critical to the planet.

Three members of the PEA team had to step up onto a pedestal while operating the machine. They were then enclosed in a type of force field that prevented them from stepping down and leaving until the machine was activated, the energy released, and a "voice" told them they could do so.

It was physically and actually activated.

On May 2, scientists discovered cracks in the ocean floor off the east coast of the United States. It was revealed that these cracks along a 25-mile stretch of the continental shelf could trigger a tsunami sending 18-foot waves towards the Mid Atlantic States.

According to Associated Press, on May 2, in Falmouth, Massachusetts, the New Millennium news site issued an abbreviated report. One can read the full article in the May, 2000, edition of the journal Geology (Reference article No.407).

This event seems to attest to the instability of the continental shelf, illustrating yet a further symptom of planet Earth's reaction to its growth stage towards the 2012 date. In addition, the Sulawesi 7.3 earthquake events and Yellowstone geyser eruption occurred. While these events were ongoing, the planets Saturn, Jupiter and Mercury slowly began to align and merge.

It is interesting to note that between May 3 and May 4, many electronic communication faults occurred, especially over the United States, mainly relating to e-mail services. In addition, a number of military communication centers heavily scanned the websites and electronic mails connected to our research group. This resulted in severe hacking and file depletion of our main Ambilac Internet site, leaving the most recent article, "Interdimensional Physics," in somewhat of an unreadable format.

In the early hours of May 4, SOHO C3 satellite images showed a large CME,[8] which was also observed on the navy military C3 satellite.[9]

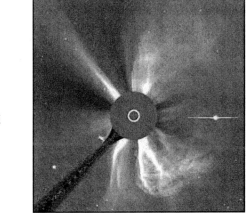

Figure 14.8
C3 Satellite Image of a CME

Radar ring activity continued to increase, which seemed to suggest that an attempt was in progress to place an electromagnetic field, or contrived "red" grid around the planet. This red grid or shield will allow only the negative force or side to enter. Therefore, it required our immediate physical intervention in order for the "natural" blue earth grid to over-ride this red grid. To further complicate matters, at this point in time, the "Love Bug" virus – "I Love You," hit all Microsoft mailing systems (exchange) causing widespread disruption at the Pentagon and other similar centers throughout the globe.

It is also important to note that prior to and on May 5, 2000, the Ambilac and several related websites received all-time visitor record hits. Also, in the period directly preceding May 5, planet Earth was subjected to mass earthquake activity, as attested to the current seismometer readings.[10]

However, immediately after the time of the crystal activation under Giza, these readings became remarkably quiet, as captured at:

http://www.cyberspaceorbit.com/quake/sizmo.html

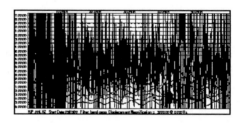

Figure 14.9 — Seismograph — USA

MAY 5, 2000 - CHAMBER ACCESS
AND CRYSTAL ACTIVATION

We will now describe one of the most important events in the history of our planet that will affect the destiny of humanity.

On May 3, 2000, a certain three individuals independently made their way to Cairo for a rendezvous. These three individuals, up to this point, had no idea as to what event was about to unfold. They only knew that their previous training and unique skills would be required. It was here that they were given the co-ordinate entry points (X's2).

This initial phase of the exercise was a risky one to say the least, due to heightened Military security on and around the Giza Plateau itself. On the night of May 3, the individuals utilized both entry points, since at that point in time it was not possible to send all three down the Bethlehem Processionway. It was here that two very old "Booby trap" explosive devices were subsequently disarmed.

The team of three carefully studied the equipment in the room, including the artifacts, glyphs and drawings that lined the walls of the room. Bear in mind that although two separate entrances were used, they both led directly to the same Chamber. The team of three then carefully vacated the site, while others simultaneously provided psychic cloaking, thus assisting with the exit process.

A number of people carefully reviewed the subsequent intelligence data that had been gathered, and a plan was devised and later put into action.

The team of three re-entered, using the Bethlehem Passageway, armed only with the knowledge that they had previously received, in order to successfully carry off this vital and delicate task. Most of what occurred during the late hours of May 4 when this team made entry, using the Bethlehem Processionway, can be heard on the Jeff Rense Sightings show archived audiotape of the interview of May 8, 2000.[11] However, what was not described in the interview was an event that occurred, of which we knew nothing, prior to having advanced the "Crystal." We were unable to share this event with anyone, as per "His" request.

We assumed that the initial bolt of energy that was fired into the disk when it locked into place, was to initiate the firing-up created to advance the grid. The team was informed that it had done well. At that point, the enclosures inside of which, as a protection they were standing, were dropped.

On the way out of the chamber, we possessed the knowledge that the team was to bring out with them a specific artifact. What we did not know at the time was the purpose and intent of this artifact. Once outside the Chamber, approximately two-thirds of the way along the Processionway, was a niche cut into the wall. The artifact was then placed inside the niche and automatically sealed in. Behind the team, the passageway lit up in a bluish/purplish light. This light ended at the location of the artifact.

When the bolt of energy, thought only to initiate the firing-up of the grid, was relayed upward (reflected upward into the pyramid itself) it entered into a body located in a sarcophagus above. This open sarcophagus, located in a chamber directly above the machinery that had been activated, contained none other than Joseph himself. Joseph had been placed in this sarcophagus, in a form of stasis awaiting this time — a time when the crystal activated the energy released, and not only entered his body, but also carried with it his life-force.

How do we know this event actually occurred? Basically, we have confirmation from two separate individuals. We also have confirmation from the

Chaldeans themselves, who, we may add, required our assistance on May 12.

As we stated previously, many people were involved, all working with their own specific and unique gifts; all with the same objectives. We knew about a few of these groups involved. However, they did not know about each other at that point in time. A further group worked on holding the existing grid in place, tightening as well as strengthening it. Once the machinery was up and running, one member of this group then found herself inside this chamber. What she witnessed, we now describe:

> He arose; his hair was thin and matted, his skin grey
> and peeling, but his eyes were "starry."
> He thanked her and said He was not yet ready. He then
> laid himself back down. She was then able to leave.

Another member of the group was sent to the plateau to see if the Chaldeans required any further assistance. She found herself outside his chamber also confirming that Joseph had returned to his body. She was also assured that indeed the Chaldeans had events well in control. At this point in time, the grid was up and holding.

In addition to the many solar anomalies observed on the Solar satellite images on May 5, the "Sun Cruiser" was also noticed, including what appeared to be another "stargate" opening.

On May 6, radar ring activity commenced in what appeared to be an effort to punch a few holes into the holding planetary grid. However, on May 8, the infamous Brookhaven Laboratories, Long Island New York, was seen to "fire up," showing heavy radar activity, in a serious attempt to dislodge or unbalance part of the existing planetary grid.   *http://www.cyberspaceorbit.com/may2.html*
http://www.cyberspaceorbit.com/may3.html

Figure 14.10 — Long Island — Radar Ring

On May 9, a number of anomalies were observed on the SOHO satellites as analyzed by Colonel Ervin.In addition, the SEC, Space Environment Center, commented there were several significant" filament eruptions observed from the south central region of the solar disk. The filaments were categorised by the SEC as "large, dense, and bright" — meaning that a large amount of solar material was contained in these features.[13]

This was also the first magnetic storm watch issued by the SEC for indices of "greater than 30"[strong storming] in quite some time. Recent watches have been for "greater than 20." However, what happened to this event that should have "hit" Earth with some severity? Could it be that the grid now in place afforded us some protection? It does appear so, from what evidence we can offer.

On May 11, Brookhaven fired up yet again, as was attested on radar-captured animations at a number of Internet sites. For one "official" explanation, the article "Solar Ups and Downs" from Space Science News is inserted below.

May 11, 2000 — In early April 2000, the Boulder sunspot number soared above 300 — the Sun was literally peppered with spots. Now, a little more than a month later, the Sun's visible disk was almost featureless, sporting just a few diminutive spots. What was going on here? Was the sunspot maximum coming or not?

"These are just normal up and downs in the sunspot cycle," explains Dr. David Hathaway, a solar physicist at the Marshall Space Flight Center who specializes in tracking and predicting sunspot activity. "On a daily or weekly basis the sunspot number can fluctuate wildly, but when we average the counts over a month they agree fairly well with our predictions that Solar Max is very near."

"The Boulder sunspot number on May 7 was 130," says Hathaway. "That's not extraordinarily low. What makes the Sun look so blank right now is the small total area that's covered by spots."

On any given day near the sunspot maximum, the areas of all the sunspots added together cover about 1200 millionths of the Sun's disk. On May 7, 2000, that number dropped all the way to 130 millionths. [Editor's note: On May 7, 2000, the sunspot area and the Boulder sunspot number were coincidentally the same — 130.]

"That's about ten times less than the average for the past two months," says Hathaway. "Meanwhile, the sunspot number is only about 25% less than the recent average. What we've got is a whole bunch of very small, hard-to-see sunspots.

http://www.spacescience.com/headlines/y2000/ast09may_1m.htm

From this point forward, we were witness to a flurry of anomalous activities, including the elongated fire scenario at Los Alamos, New Mexico. Then, on May 13, courtesy of the C3 Solar satellite, we were privileged to witness an exciting display of the planets Jupiter, Mercury, Saturn and Venus, with the emergence of M45, better known as the Pleiades.

On May 11, we were then summoned back to the Plateau – for exactly what reason, we were not sure. Two men entered the Bethlehem Processionway, where they encountered a group of Chaldeans who informed them that they had sealed off all accesses to the Chambers located beneath the Great Pyramid. All accesses, they said, except for one — but did not indicate which one, or why it was not sealed up. Before leaving, the two men held a two-hour discussion with the Chaldeans.

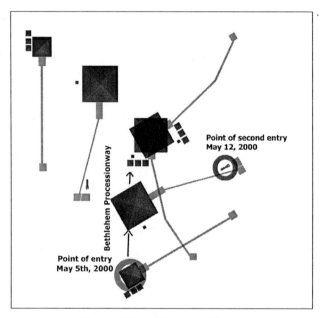

Figure 14.12 — Plateau model

On May 12, a team of three was sent into another chamber, located on a separate part of the Plateau, for which the entry was relatively straightforward. Inside, the team was met by the same Chaldeans encountered the previous day, in the Bethlehem Processionway. The Chaldeans explained that they would have performed this next task themselves, but they were unsure of a few of the instructions that were carved into the walls. They were concerned that they would make a mistake. Although one of the team could read the text, to be on the safe side, they left to check with others in order to verify the translation.

The complication arose from the fact that there were two types of instructional writings. The first was in Hieratic script (a cursive form of Hieroglyphic writing which the Egyptians used for everyday writing) and the other was in Hieroglyph form.

Basically, the writings stated that when fired up, this machine would draw on external power sources to power the grid. It seems that the machinery located in the other Chamber was powered by internal, stored, energy. Prior to returning to assist the Chaldeans in this task, we contacted the group whom we knew possessed the experience with the grid. They responded very quickly and were in position to hold the grid, in the event that there would be a delay in delivering power to the grid when this transfer was made.

Fortunately, as it transpired, the transition went reasonably well. However, what the team of three did not know, until they were inside the Chamber (causing a slight delay), was that Joseph had instructed one of the Light Workers to "cloak the chamber." The chamber as well as its entrance point was located in a very exposed area near the plateau where the heavy military presence was on high alert. Thus, additional cloaking was necessary. This requirement was carried out immediately and the process ran smoothly. Once completed, on a "screen display" appeared the following message: "You have done well. Thank you."

Prior to the change-over, the team reported that the machinery made a humming sound at various pitches. Once the change-over was complete, the sound became a steady peaceful regular hum. On May 15, seismometer readings began to increase somewhat, while at the same time the LASCO C2 images showed massive Coronal Mass Ejections taking place. The following day, May 16, as attested by the C2 images once more, our old friend, the "Solar Cruiser" or Plasma Carrier, showed itself! And on Planet Earth, we were subjected to a number of reported large earthquakes.

Presently, events are occurring at warp speed. In addition, two significant events of crucial importance occurred recently.

On May 21, from observing the activities via LASCO C2, it appeared that Revelation, Chapter 12, verse 3 was being acted out! Although the images were withdrawn from public view, it came to our attention that a massive CME occurred while the Pleiades group was directly north of the sun.

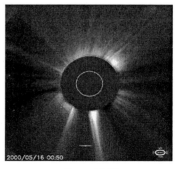

Figure 14.13
The "Solar Cruiser"

> *"And there was seen another sign in the heavens; and behold a great dragon, having seven heads and ten horns and on his head diadems. (crowns)"*

— Revelation

Are we talking of the Pleiades here, the seven sisters, standing directly on the crown with the CME's as horns or rays? It certainly appears to be so! In addition to this observation, the union of Joseph and Mary (Isis) could be observed symbolically in the tryst between Jupiter and Venus.

Figure 14.14 —- Solar Image Showing the Pleiades

Was this what the Pope had in mind when he arrived at Fatima in Portugal on May 13? His intention was the beautification of two of the three Fatima visionary children. After speaking with the sole surviving visionary, Sister Lucia, the Pope ordered the Vatican to prepare the Third Secret of Fatima to be released to the public. Thus, in doing so, he released the energy necessary for the appearance of Isis to carry out her role in the Natural Law!

Beginning on May 13, 2000 and continuing for a total of four consecutive days, a very special person was visited by Isis/Mary. A Pregnant Mary was standing with a very strong wind blowing about her. Make no mistake. "He" will be born on December 21, 2000.

When Mary visited with the three Children at Fatima, She instructed them to return on the same day, for the next consecutive six months. She said that in the seventh month, She would reappear — at which time a real miracle could be witnessed . . . We refer to this as the "Birth Event."

Through natural evolution and over aeons of time, the key pressure points of the global grid are about to be shifted. As the earth prepares for its jump into that time line, certain symptoms will be experienced, such as the movement and adjustment of the earth's tectonic plates while the earth adjusts to accompany this transition. As one will witness, this results in a traumatic post-shock series of earthquakes, volcanoes, etc. There are presently precursor events occurring that will trigger these changes.

If we go back in time to the year 1947, contact was established with the Zetas, or "greys" (Zeta-Reticuli is a star system in the constellation Reticulum, visible only in the Southern Hemisphere) who explained the above forthcoming scenario to Majestic, better known as the MJ-12 Group.

MJ-12 is an ultra top secret Research and Development Intelligence Operation that was established by President Truman on September 24, 1947 in light of the events at Roswell, New Mexico, where a UFO supposedly crashed and grey aliens/ alien hybrids were captured. The group, also known as The Majestic Twelve Operation, Majestic 12, Majic 12, MAJCOM, or MJ-12, was created under an executive order on September 24, 1947. The panel was empowered to review all available evidence and data collected by the government, military and intelligence agencies.

MJ-12 was a "Committee" set up inside the NSC (National Security Council). In 1954, President Eisenhower signed the Secret Executive Order, "Order Number 54-12."

Included in the scenario was the explanation that, coupled with the effects of the earth, would be the imminent deletion of the east and west coasts of the United States. This effect would be caused by the earth readjusting its tectonic plates in preparation for the transition.

It is at this point that the Zetas offered a possible alternative scenario. The deals were struck and goals set. A program was initiated and expanded rapidly. This program incorporated the knowledge of how to access time lines. Utilization of these lines offered the time required to side-step "natural law."

We want to point out that this scenario may not be acceptable, since it locks the existing Entities into this time frame; in effect, enslaving us by disabling us from evolving to our next level. From what we know and feel, humankind is "screaming" for the right to exercise our free will choice, i.e., to follow Him into the next level – known as ascension.

He heard our call to exercise our free will choice and is now here to ensure that our rights are protected. "They" are no match for "Him" and that is why the Zetas exited recently.

However, there are still a few who will resist the natural law right up to the bitter end, as they continue to implement a plan gone sour.

It is apparent that beyond our sun, the "force" is parked outside. They are not in our visible spectrum, since they are in another time frame. This time frame will shift when a hole in the grid is created, and they will then begin to execute any plan they have devised.

Brookhaven may be the key to this.

Ephriam will claim his birthright soon, and they know this; so they will attempt to complete their plan as soon as possible.

THE GRID

The function of the grid in place, encircling planet Earth, is one of stabilization, or filtering. The origin of construction (refer to Chapter 11, "The Great Experiment") is a combined human and Extra-Terrestrial creation, and was set in place to diffuse abnormal fluctuations, such as the effects of massive CME's and solar flares, etc. At certain points in time, "we" were apt to align at a position where planet Earth was under a stronger influence from one or more astral bodies than would have otherwise been the norm. Alignment, therefore, is the crux of this grid. Existence or non-existence is substantiated solely by this control of alignment.

What we termed earlier as the "Red Grid" can be utilized to re-direct excess energy into specific targets. One has only to follow the profuse "radar rings" on the satellite weather maps to follow this scenario. The Blue, or Purple Grid allows for the equal re-distribution of excess energy.

Many remote viewers and the gifted individuals known as "travelers" are able to enter through a window, or portal in this grid, and exit out of another at a different time and place. These travelers know and can locate the points of these "windows" along the grid. Therefore, by altering the grid, as occurred recently, to our overall advantage, in effect, we have changed the location of these "windows." In addition, we have changed time to our "natural time," thereby exercising our free will choice.

Based on the alignment, to which we previously referred, time actually denotes the density of light that is realized at a given point in space. In basic terms, it could be said that the grid itself has no time or space within, but is a flowing continuum; at the same time, one must locate the "windows" of entry and exit.

Gridworkers on May 5 could actually see the free will choice made, as pinpoints of Light over Terra. These gradually increased until Terra was covered in a complete mass of Light. These points of Light were the peoples of Terra joining in making their choice, helping to align and make strong the blue, or purple grid. Once the choice was made known and Terra was lit, the grid was pushed in close to earth, where it remains strong. Although this grid does not negate the red grid, it isolates the red grid to Terra. No longer can others enter into our co-ordinate without our permission. However, the red grid can still function in this co-ordinate, beneath the blue grid.

For additional clarification of how this grid was constructed, and its function and operation, please see the Appendix, "The Universal Grid."

We were made very aware of Brookhaven National Laboratory on May 5, especially since the laboratories stopped the work of the collider at the time. If a hole is punched through the grid, we will observe the fleets entering over New York, where they will make their presence known, and thus be visible. The people of Terra did not strike the deal; only a few took that choice into their own hands. The ones who did, will then know what occurs when Natural Law, or the Covenant, is broken.

If this is allowed to occur, the war being fought near Jupiter will enter our co-ordinate and we will be drawn into it. The Great Deception lies in the deal that was struck. The deal itself was a deception, setting in place the technology to allow the take-over of Terra — to enslave her people and prevent Ascension. By being prevented from moving to the next level, we would remain where we are, on the course where we are headed. This would result in the near-extinction of the people of Terra, leaving the planet and its resources to those who would desire this piece of real estate. Those who remain after this take-over would become drones for the new occupants.

We have made the choice not to allow this!

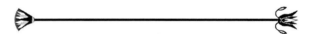

Notes

1. *The Prophecy* - A film starring Christopher Walken.
   > *An ancient Bible is found on the body of a dead angel that contains a previously unknown chapter of the Bible telling of a second war to be waged by angels on earth. That war is about to occur, led by the Archangel Gabriel (Christopher Walken), whose jealousy of God's love for humans has turned him malevolent and bloodthirsty.*

   http://www.hollywoodjesus.com/prophecy.htm

2. *The Fifth Element* - 1998, a film starring Bruce Willis
   > *Every five thousand years a door opens between the dimensions. In one dimension lies the universe and all of its multitude of life forms. In another exists an element made not of earth, air, fire or water but of anti-energy, anti-life. This "thing," this darkness, waits patiently at the threshold of the universe for an opportunity to extinguish all life and all light.*

   http://www.fifthelement.co.uk/frame_x.html

3.   *The Matrix* - 1999 Warner Brothers Film
     *The Matrix is everywhere. It's all around us, here even in this room. You can
     see it out your window, or on your television. You feel it when you go to work,
     or go to church or pay your taxes. It is the world that has been pulled over your
     eyes to blind you from the truth... Unfortunately, no one can be told what the
     Matrix is. You have to see it for yourself*

     http://neomatrix88.virtualave.net/

4.   http://julieking.htmlplanet.com/

5.   *Flash Radar.* Site of a dedicated radar ring researcher, to be found at:

     http://www.toledolink.com/~flash/flashx.html

6.   **On April 28-30 a mysterious torpedo zooms towards the sun Solar Toredo,
     Angels and Lockheed-Martin.**
     After the Torpedo [see below] disappeared behind the solar south pole NASA
     cut the data-feed: 20000430_0654; MISSING FILES; 20000430_1054

     http://www.cyberspaceorbit.com/text/newz18x.htm
     http://www.cyberspaceorbit.com/april5.html

7.   http://sohowww.nascom.nasa.gov/data/realtime/javagifs/2000505_0042c3.gif

8.   http://lasco-www.nrl.navy.mil/

9.   http://tuvpo.htmlplanet.com/deprem/sismo.html

10. http://broadcast.com/shows/endoftheline/00archives.html

11. http://www.cyberspaceorbit.com/text/newz21x.htm

12. http://www.cyberspaceorbit.com/sun/5-9col.htm

13. http://www.rhichome.bnl.gov/AP/status

Chapter 15

Synopsis of Volume 1 With An Introduction to Volume 2

A PICTORIAL OVERVIEW

At the beginning of this book, we stated that it would be an extremely complex task to present in one book all the information in our possession that has been deciphered thus far. In the previous 14 chapters, we have condensed a diverse array of verifiable data that highlights the key elements or pieces of the gigantic jig saw we are attempting to construct. Occasionally it may appear that we pass over what would seem to the reader to be a critical piece of data. However, the enormous task we have set before us is complex and there is only so much material we are able to present in a single volume. For that reason, we offer the following "pictorial walkthrough" that takes us to the May 12, 2000 star alignment. These diagrams will serve as an introduction in preparation for Volume Two.

As we mentioned in our introduction, the difficulty is knowing when and where the point of origin commenced. Thus, the same can be said for determining the "end" point, the Alpha – Omega. One of the greatest philosophical discussions in the history of humankind debates the very question as to the beginning and the end (and beyond) of life as we know it. Since the answer is infinity, shall we ever really know?

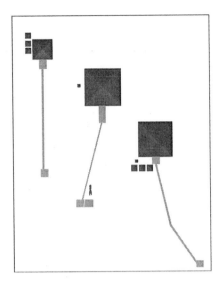

Figure 15.1— Plateau - Top View

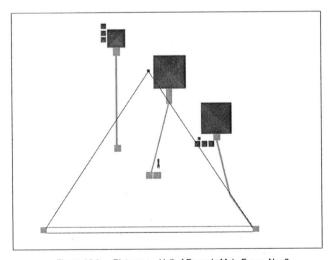

Figure 15.2 — Plateau —   Hall of Records Main Frame No. 2

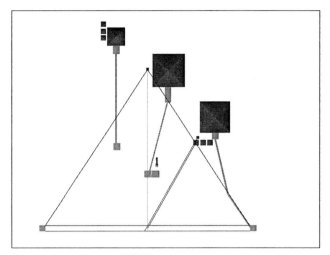

Figure 15.3 — Plateau — Main Frame No. 2

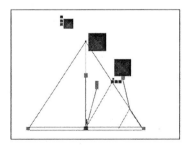

Figure 15.4 — Plateau — Main Frame No. 3

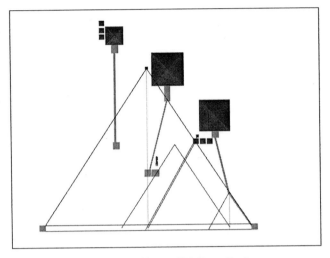

Figure 15.5 — Plateau - Main Frame No. 4

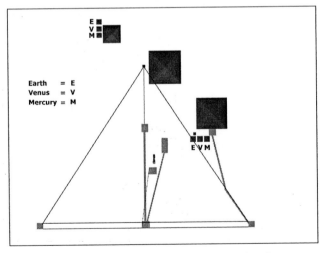

Figure 15.6 — Plateau — Hall of Records and Tomb Locations

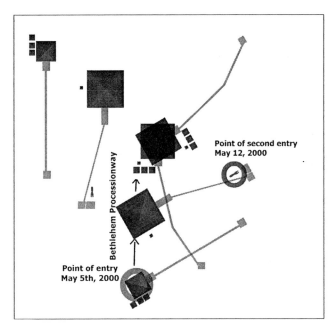

Figure 15.7 — Full Plateau — Model 120 Degrees Rotation,
The Bethlehem Processionway

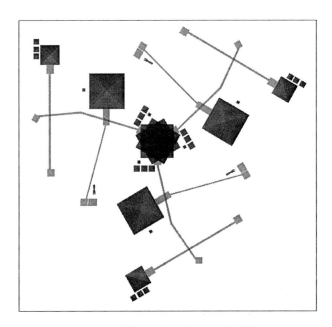

Figure 15.8 — Full Plateau Model 120 — 0-120-240 Degrees

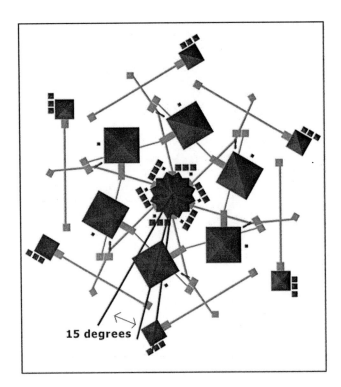

Figure 15.9
May 5th
Plateau Alignment
– Star Chart

Figure 15.10
May 5th
Star Alignment

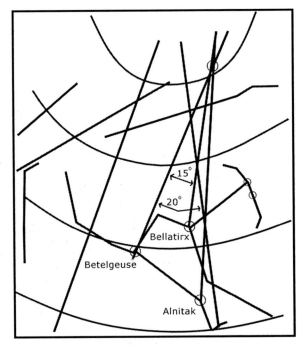

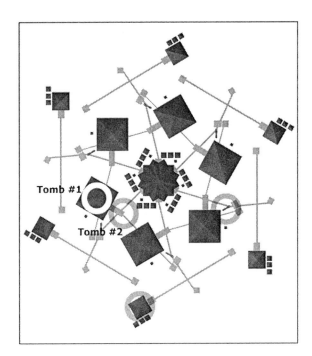

Figure 15.11
Overview of
Volume 2 A

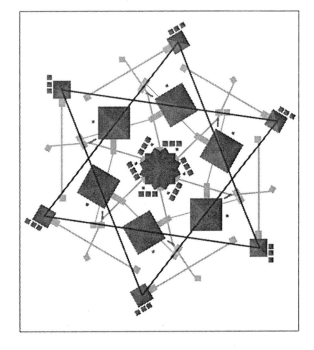

Figure 15.12
Overview of
Volume 2 B

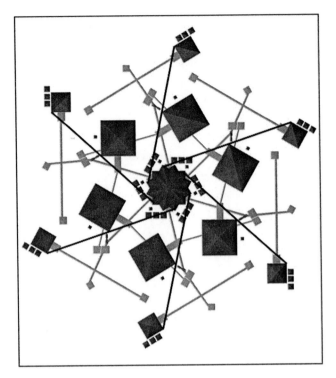

Figure 15.13 — Overview of Volume 2 C

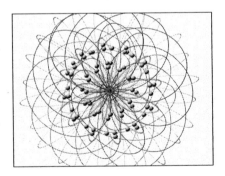

Figure 15.14 — All 12 Houses — Top View

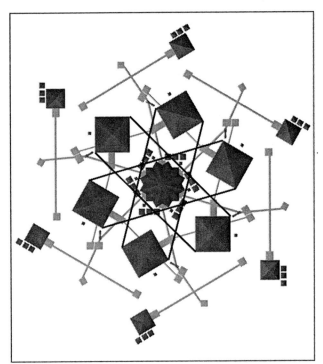

Figure 15.15
Volume 2 D

Figure 15.16
Volume 2 E

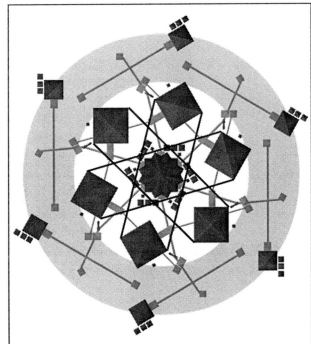

Appendix A

Parallel Universes

We sit on the brink of amazing new discoveries in the fields of physics, archeology, biology, astronomy and others that are fueling a major shift in the consciousness of being. We are becoming different humans. Our understanding of who we are is becoming fuller and more complete as we awaken to a new perception of ourselves. We are beginning to sense that physical reality only appears to be all that is and that there is a parallel reality or parallel realities in which we also exist and from which physical reality is manifested.

One of the awkward aspects of this new awareness is our inability to describe it and explain it in the language of logic and physical description. The parallel realities seem to operate under different sets of rules than does physical reality. One can step into some of these parallel realities during meditation or other "altered states of consciousness" and begin to describe the experience, but the description is limited by the need to use words that have been developed for use in the reality of material existence. Often, when one is able to move into one of these parallel realities, the feeling is simply one of "knowing" that transcends normal logic and explanation.

One of these parallel realities is described as holographic: a state of being wherein everything is everywhere all the time; space and time as we know it cease to exist. From this state, with practice one can choose to attune consciousness to any aspect of being. It is a vast territory ripe for exploration.

Another of these parallel realities is one of mathematical formulas and geometrical constructs. It is from this state that "Sacred Geometry" is born and has meaning. Within this reality, one can begin to understand the geometry of electro-chemical creation of DNA and the energetic patterns of relationships between star systems and ourselves and how it is that we could be called "Star Children" by native tribal legend. Also, it is in this reality where we can understand the resonant relationships between form and well-being in the material reality.

From the perspective of these realities it is possible to see one's life in an evolutionary context or to experience the "magic" of creation and to realize that not only are we more than mortal physical beings but that we always exist in all realities. In this level of understanding, we know we are gods with the infinite power of the universe at our disposal. In this level, we know that there is nothing outside of ourselves because we are One.

From the perspective of the holographic-energetic reality, it is easy to see how we create our own reality. It is easy to sympathize with, and have compassion for, ourselves as mortal human ego-centered beings who are controlled by our desire to control our physical world with physical acts in the name of self-satisfaction, creating chaos, pollution and disease in the process, and how Jesus, bleeding and nailed to the cross, cries out, "Forgive them, Father, for they know not what they do."

We are coming to an evolutionary point, however, of knowing what we do, and why, and how the physical world is a joint creation of our limited understandings. When enough of us reach expanded levels of understanding, the world begins to change rapidly and radically. Until then, we see the world as limited and we need to get all we can for our own protection and well-being. In so doing, we miss opportunity after opportunity to tap into the abundance of the universe and co-create unlimited well-being for all. The legendary Shamballa and the Fountain of Youth are right in front of our eyes but we are blinded by self-imposed restriction that the material world is all there is.

Wayne Moody
October, 2000

Appendix B

Universal Grid

Throughout the universe is a grid. This Universal Grid looks three-dimensional, but it does not have the aspects of time or space. At each juncture is a mathematical two-number set, acting as co-ordinates. Therefore, it is basically a vector matrix and everything within the grid is pure energy that fluctuates in frequency at various sectors of the grid; thus making it interdimensional.

Travel within the grid, or within the universe, is by thought. Therefore, it is instantaneous, involving no time and no space. Consequently, travel is from one set or sequence of coordinates to another. For example, to travel from A to B, you may think of a place or time, or both. But that thought equates to a mathematical thought energy. Thus, one travels from point A to point B via the coordinates.

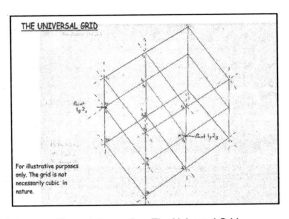

Figure 1 Appendix – The Universal Grid

The Earth Blue Grid

The Universal Grid surrounds everything in our universe, including our earth, our solar system and the stars we observe in our sky. At various sectors of the grid, specific stars, galaxies and planets exist, by the combination of grid points that are in that sector. Everything in that sector will have a certain thought configuration and frequency, and therefore, be related to every other object in that sector. Consequently, certain configurations in the stars surrounding our solar system will be found within our solar system also. In addition, configurations in our solar system are found on each planet in that system, including the planet Earth.

The configuration of certain constellations and solar system patterns form a grid surrounding Earth. Therefore, this earth grid can be mapped over the earth's surface from point to point.

Since this is a mathematical energy grid, it can be manipulated by thought energy in the same manner as travel through the Universal Grid can occur. It is basically a matrix grid within the Universal Matrix Grid. This earth grid was named "Blue Grid" because it was shown as being a blue light grid surrounding Earth.

The Red Grid

An additional grid was identified as being red in color; subsequently, it was termed the "Red Grid."

This red grid is an electromagnetic grid placed around the earth using alien technology. When further clarification was required, the information supplied was that a contract occurred between those of earth with a race called the Zeta Reticuli. It was this race that gave the technology for the Red Grid to be placed around the Earth. (I have since read various articles relating to such a contract, but I did not know of this prior to these visions.)

However, when the contract came to an end, the Zeta people could not leave Earth, for they had been trapped here; and the way the technology was used was foreign to them.

Because thought energy can also affect the Red Grid, and vortices (holes) can be created within, in 1995, the Zetas were given the opportunity to leave. Many, in fact, did leave. A few stayed here to observe how the technology would further be used. These observers are on a suicidal mission and are aware of that fact; but this Zeta group is no longer a part of the original contract.

The Red Grid is utilized for any technological manipulations that are hidden from public view. If thought, directed using the Blue Grid, is used to create a vortex in the Red Grid (which requires a particular frequency sequence), airplanes will literally fall from the sky.

Any manipulations to the Blue Grid would be obvious to the eye, although most people would not realize this unless they know the layout of the Blue Grid. For example, a created earthquake can be seen.

I purposely did not attempt to map the Red Grid, and coordinates were not given for it. Any manipulations can be done through the Blue Grid to counteract the Red Grid.

THE STRINGS OF THE HARP - USES OF THE RED GRID

As previously illustrated, the grids consist of intersecting planes. The Blue Grid consists of planes extending to infinity, as part of the Universal Grid. The Red Grid consists of planes extending only to Earth's limits, including Earth's atmosphere, inner core and perhaps her moon.

Energy travels through these grid planes from co-ordinate to co-ordinate. Thus, if limits can be set on the particle spread in that travel, a pulse effect can occur. These limits can be set by setting the strength of the bond between particles, a stronger bond creating more pulse.

If physically created energy from earth is sent through the grid, speed must be included in the equation. This will ultimately affect the final pulse strength. A physical radio or radar frequency and accelerated particle frequencies are two types of physically created energy.

Physical energy can be increased in strength by drawing energy from the electromagnetic fields of earth, and by using the grid for transfer. An increase in strength can also be gained by drawing energy through the grid from other areas of the grid.

Therefore, energy can be drawn from the earth's electromagnetic field, set at a particular frequency, sent along the grid while gathering energy from the grid as it travels, and returned at greater strength to the earth's electromagnetic field at its place of arrival.

Do we have the technology to do this? I believe we do. However, this technology is yet to be fine-tuned, since presently all parameters on the energy are not known. Therefore, total control of the energy is not complete and various side effects can occur, such as unwanted earthquakes, storms, and so on. The reason for this is that as energy is drawn into the pulse, a temporary imbalance is created in the grid. That energy, then sent along the grid, can create earth changes at the point of arrival (which was the purpose of sending it); but the imbalance can create side effects anywhere along the plane of travel. If the existing tectonic plates of earth are then brought into the equation, the side effects can then be sent along the plate fault lines.

Another parameter to consider is that of life on Earth. Any alteration to the grid will cause alteration in the organisms of Earth, as everything in a grid sector contains the same basic structure. Side effects of pulse use of the grid for this parameter will result in an imbalance causing various diseases; for example, mental and hormonal imbalance, cancer, and physical deformities. This could ultimately be used as a means to control the evolution of a species.

If additional and unexpected parameters were included, the effects would not easily be predicted. The electromagnetic field of a comet for example, could create manifestations not expected in the matrix. Just as a solar coronal mass ejection can alter the path of a comet, the electromagnetic field of a comet could alter a pulse being sent through the grid. The same may apply with solar and stellar emissions.

If the pulse of time balances earth, it can therefore be seen that manipulation of pulses through the grid can cause an imbalance, requiring time to be re-set.

GRID ACTIVATION

On May 5, 2000, the Blue Grid was seen as purple, due to the change in frequency of the grid for the alignment to be carried out successfully; thus being changed to a higher frequency. The grid was connected to the crystal grid via the sacred sites, with Giza as the fulcrum at that time.

When the peoples of Earth joined hands and made the decision to defend Earth as their own, the grid became stronger. This was affected by pulling the whole of the grid closer to the earth, thereby creating a tighter and stronger web.

When looking at the grid now, it is a purple haze around the earth, with no definite energy lines visible. It was necessary for the choice to be made and the grid to be strengthened, before the grid could be changed over to the new and ancient energy source. No change would have occurred if we, as people of Earth, had not *asked* through our decision to join hands.

When the energy source was connected to the Great Pyramid at Giza on May 12, 2000, no change occurred to the grid itself, and to date, the Grid remains strong.

Julie King
Australia 2000

Appendix C

Summary of the Thesis and Research for the Giza-Genesis Disclosure Series

Using the information provided in the Books of Genesis and Exodus, combined with archaeo-astronomical data, crucial evidence has been discovered concerning the true purpose and meaning of the complete physical layout of the Pyramid Complex on the Giza Plateau, Egypt. The findings offer an incredible and profound re-interpretation of our origins both here on planet Earth and elsewhere. These findings not only show our true heritage as Homo sapiens, but also, the make-up of our solar system and beyond.

While analyzing this Genesis connection, the group believed that, in part, we are about to experience a return of what the Ancient Egyptians terms "Zep Tepi," or "The First Time." This is the time that began from the primeval oceans (Nun) to Horus and the redemption of Osiris, god of the underworld and resurrection – a period the ancients referred to as the "Time of the Gods," recorded in the heavens above. This was visualized and reflected in the display of the celestial orbs and constellations where the main "players" were such "gods" as Ra (our sun), Osiris (Orion), Isis (Sirius), and Thoth (the moon).

By utilizing the ages of the biblical characters in Genesis and relating them to the 360 degrees of a circle, it was discovered that they provided a "star chart," with Adam as the first star in the set. It is important to remember that we establish the Garden of Eden as the origin from which all direction began. Everything, including stars and planets east of that point of origin has very distinctive reference co-ordinates, i.e., North, South, East and West. North was established as "O" degrees, and Adam was placed at this point. A complete cycle in our mathematics is 360 degrees. When Adam was 130 years old, he had a son named Seth. Afterwards, he lived another 800 years for a total of 930 years. What is important here are the figures 130 and 930. To triangulate the co-ordinates from Adam to Seth, we must transpose Adam's life span into degrees. This method was utilized throughout, to eventually complete our star chart.

Using a pyramid model of Khufu, it was overlaid inside the Genesis model by aligning the pyramid's outer casing (south side) with the Enoch line, and the center of the pit found in the subterranean chamber, with the Lamech line. "Light beams" were then directed down the two shafts into the Queen's Chamber, rotating the model until the northern shaft intersects exactly with the spot marked Adam. Consequently, the southern shaft lines up exactly with Seth, thus reinforcing the theory that both shafts are aimed at a downward direction, as they do not exit the pyramid.

Next, the angle that the pyramid model intersects our Enoch line is slightly greater than 65.90277 degrees, or the point where our Methuselah line should have intersected with Enoch. Using a new meridian line on the pyramid model, it was discovered that at this precise location, Noah aligns with the entry to the passageway to the Queen's Chamber (our old meridian line is dead center), therefore, establishing a "0" degree alignment. Both shafts in the King's Chamber exit the pyramid, unlike those found in the Queen's Chamber. The same will hold true (no exit) for the two proposed shafts that extend from the Grand Gallery.

By combining this method in conjunction with other testable data, it was discovered that not only was the group able to identify and locate the three tombs of Osiris, Elnil and Joseph, but also, it was able to ascertain the true purpose and location of what has been referred to as the "Ark of the Covenant." The covenant, however, seems to be in the form of a large natural crystal deep below one of the Queen's Pyramids of Khufu, and was in fact placed to provide, in conjunction with other crystals sited at sacred spaces around the planet, a protective shield around planet Earth. The shield was to protect the atmosphere from geomagnetic solar storms and associated solar activity, whether natural, or human-made. This crystal is protected itself by an energy field, or "blessing." It is believed that it may only be accessed by the correct DNA, genetically inherited, and by acoustic command.

We have already started to witness increased solar activity coupled with large Coronal Mass Ejections originating from our sun. The result of these harmful emissions may provide the catalyst for an ancient race of beings, lying in stasis below the Gaza Plateau, to awaken in time for the May 5 planetary alignment. This alignment is also a combined stellar alignment, where our sun, Saturn and Jupiter are in complete alignment with the star Betelgeuse (the Bethlehem star) in the constellation of Orion. In addition, if one were to draw a line through the three belt stars of Orion at this exact time, it would center directly upon Mars, thus providing an energy flow towards Earth and the Giza Plateau. In essence, this affords a cosmic portal or "stargate," where inter-dimensional flow of matter and beings will be realized.

Appendix D

Time Line

1. Arrival of the reptilians, Orions and Sirians, on Earth

2. Arrival of Pleiadians

3. Genesis dates for Jacob and the DNA separation work

4. Genesis dates for Jacob becoming Israel; thus, the conversion of Jacob from a Sirian (reptilian) and the beginning of the Pleiadian "One God" race, and the exit of the Sirians . . . leaving just the Orions and Pleiadians

Clarification: If Jacob brought these beings from other worlds, that would mean that they did not exist on Earth before that time. However, other time lines indicate that reptilians were here long before Jacob. And then, we have other indications from other historic time lines (Egyptian, Sumerian, etc.) that these beings were here long before Jacob, who is relatively late on the time line.

To answer the above...
Basically, how long is a piece of string??

CAVEAT
    We may have to re-evaluate our thinking concerning geological chronology and terminology. For example, an increasing number of Paleontologists contend that the "traditional" dates offered in this field may be seriously out of synch, that is, millions of years younger!

Today, using new techniques, it is possible to "create" a fossilized sample overnight; therefore questioning the traditionally held beliefs and "dates" of the dinosaur and reptile period. Bearing this in mind, we attempt to demonstrate the chronology relevant to our work on the Giza-Genesis connection. Due to the many aeons involved and the many misinterpretations, it is only possible to develop a chronology as we see it, within this work. Or, in other words, it must be appreciated that it is impossible to calculate any actual dates or a "time" as we know it.

We must also remember that we are also dealing with an additional complexity, i.e., the integration and intervention of the "great experiment" involving life on this planet, whereby a number of races have been "interfering" with their own genetics.

1.   The accepted Genesis Genealogy – brief overview

ABRAM m SARAI (later SARAH)

ABRAM (via HAGAR) and SARAH
=
ISHMAEL   ISAAC

ISAAC m REBEKAH
=
ESAU and JACOB

JACOB (changes to ISRAEL) m RACHEL
=
JOSEPH and BENJAMIM

JOSEPH m AS'ENATH
=
EUPHRAIM and MANASEH

2. In combination with the above, our Time Line as described in full in the text.

STAR CHART AND ALIGNMENT

Adam – Seth – Enosh – Kenan –
Mahalelel - Jared – Enoch – Methuselah – Lamech

Noah

EARTH— TWO SETS OF LINEAGES
First Lineage
Sun and Adam, Seth, Enosh, Kenan, Mahalel, Jared
Adam is point of origin – Zero degrees in "Garden of Eden"
(Circumstances under the influential force of the
Alignments of the starsfrom Orion and Sirius.)
Orion-Pleiadian lineage
Nahor (Orion) father of Terah
Terah father of Abram (Orion - Pleiadian) and Haran (Sirian)
Alcyon in Pleiades (Taurus constellation)
Adam (Terah)
Abram our sun
Abraham – planet Earth

("No longer shall you be called Abram; all be Abraham,
for I am making you father of a host of nations.")

Second lineage
Jared lineage - Chaldean or Nordic –
associated with Euphrates Haran

(Third Lineage)
Nahor – Seth (reptilian) lineage and associated with Tigris
Earth becomes Isaac at second location (Venus previously);
Jacob or "Israel" in present position in Solar System.

(When Earth reaches next position occupied by Mars.
It will be known as "Joseph.")

We are about to enter into this time.

LOT
(Equated to the Third Lineage and the last battle of the last time)
(The Abram lineage is the first one and Hagar is lineage number two)

The Eighth Day

At this point the *reptilian* form is "lost" (the skin is shed).
" . . . *keep my covenant throughout the ages*"

The Three Wise Men, the High Council, Receive Gifts

The three representatives from the three lineages -
Orion, Pleiades and Syrian representatives -
promised the future harvest, now soon to unfod.
"Two nations are in your womb, two peoples are
quarrelling while still within you; but one shall surpass the
other, and the older shall serve the younger."

Esau, the eldest one nation,
who was and remains of the reptilian race.
Jacob – youngest, the second nation Isaac was 60 years old and
still possessed the vestige of a *reptilian* tail.

The gravesite of Isaac is the same as that of Osiris.

Esau sold birthright to Jacob.
Jacob— Isaac's blessing giving him possession all that is above ground.

Esau is blessed but must dwell below ground
while simultaneously serving his brother
until at such time he "becomes restive."

Sarah is buried on Giza.

Abraham is buried next to Sarah in the Hall of Records.
Jacob is introduced to the moon. (Jacob's ladder) or
what we now term, "monoliths."

Jacob now leaves Isaac and goes to Haran (Chaldeans),
meets Laban, son of Nahor (reptilian race).

Jacob weds Leah
Jacob - Rachel
Joseph
The ancestral god, (The Pleiadians) god of Abraham

Jacob and Laban,
(Tomb Number One, or the pyramid of Menkaura)

Esau meets Jacob with 400 men.
Jacob divides the camp into two factions:
the division of the *reptilian* and human life forms.

Jacob meets the "angel" (Pleiadian) across the Euphrates.
Jacob loses his "tail."
"Jacob" is now called "Israel" or earth in its present position.

*"You shall no longer be spoken of as Jacob, but as Israel,
because you have contended with divine human being."*

Jacob constructs an altar at "Bethel" adjacent to the site of
Menkaura (Laban's site).
This is "Tomb" Number Two, near and under the pyramid of Khafre.
God then gives Jacob the lands and rights that had previously belonged to
Abraham and Isaac.
That is Bethel or the Giza Plateau.

Rachel gives birth to Benjamin and dies.

Joseph builds a monument to Rachel,
marking her grave with a pyramid on the plateau,
possibly the satellite pyramid of Khafre's pyramid.

*"Rachel died, and she was buried on
the way to Ephrath (that is, Bethlehem)."*

Isaac dies at 180 years.

Esau and Jacob bury him in tomb number one on the Giza Plateau.
Esau now departs for the highlands, se'ir, or Mars.

Joseph buries Jacob tomb number two.

Joseph dies at 110 years.
Embalmed and placed in coffin.

Appendix E

Figure Enlargements

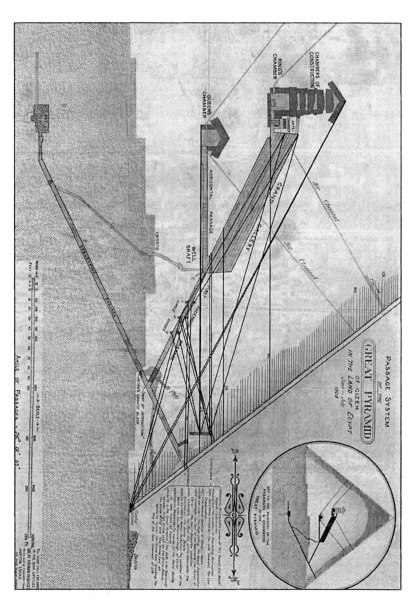

Figure 6.4 - Great Pyramid - Internal Layout No. 1 - [as view on page 91]

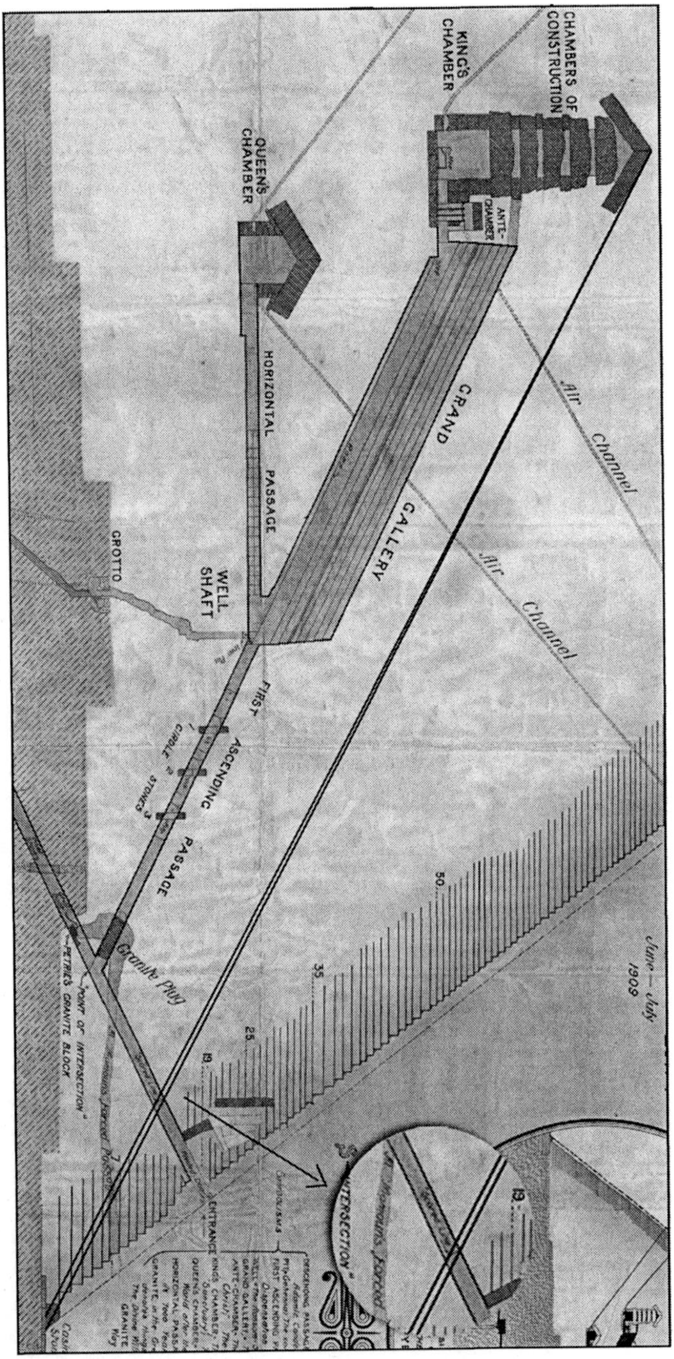

Figure 6.5 - Great Pyramid internal layout No. 2

[as viewed on page.92]

Figure 6.6 - The Great Pyramid Entrance

[as view on page 93]

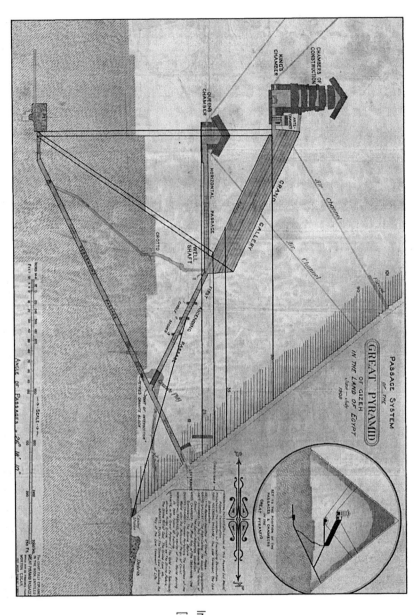

Figure 6.8
Great Pyramid
Internal Layout NO. 3
[as view on page 96]

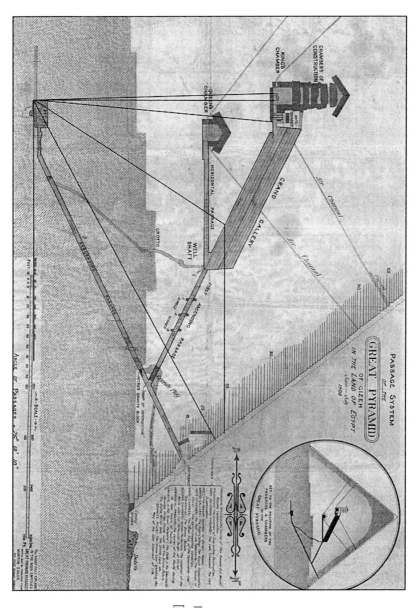

Figure 6.9
Great Pyramid
Internal Layout No.4
[as view on page 97]

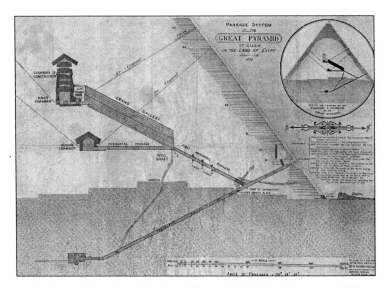

Figure 7.1 - Great Pyramid – General Internal Model - [as view on page 101]

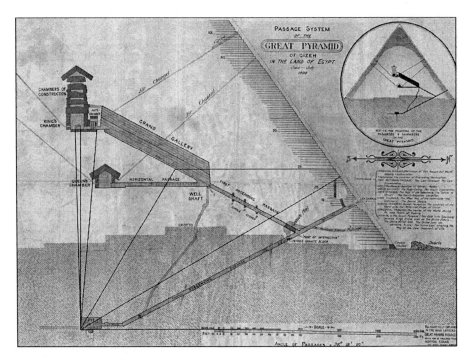

Figure 7.2 - Great Pyramid - Internal South Wall - [as view on page 102]

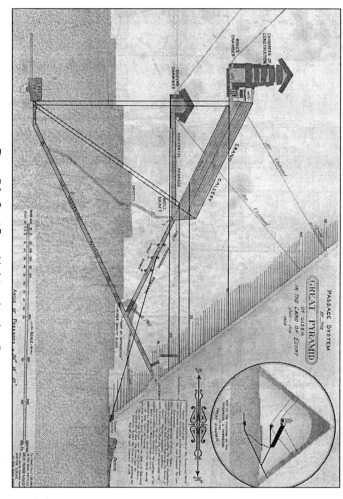

Figure 7.3 - Great Pyramid - internal north wall

[as viewed on page 103]

Bibliography

Aldred, C .*The Egyptians*. London: Thames and Hudson 1961.

Betro, Maria, C. *Hieroglyphs, The Writings of Ancient Egypt*. New York: Abbeville Press, 1996.

Budge, W. *By the Nile and Tigris, 2 Vols.* Cambridge, 1925.

Clayton, P.A. *Chronicle of the Pharaohs*. London: Thames and Hudson, 1994.

Davidson, J., Morris, M. *The Pyramids – An Enigma Solved.* New York: Dorset Press, 1988.

Fix, R Wm. *Pyramid Odyssey.* Toronto: John Wiley and Sons, 1978.

Lehner, M. *The Complete Pyramids.* London: Thames and Hudson, 1997.

Lemesurier, P. *The Great Pyramid Decoded.* New York: Dorset, 1976.

Manley, B. *Penguin Historical Atlas of Ancient Egypt.* London: Penguin,1996.

Moroney, A *Pathway to Atlantis,* Australia: Singleton NSW, 1998.

Morton, E. *The Great Pyramid Passages and Chambers. Vol 1.* Glasgow Bone and Hulley, 1910.

Shaw, I., Nicholson. *The British Museum Dictionary of Ancient Egypt.* London: BCA 1995.

Smythe, P. *The Great Pyramid.* (from the original of 1888) . New Jersey: Crown Publishers, 1978.

The Authors

Howard Middleton-Jones

An author, investigative archaeologist, Egyptologist and frequent visitor to Egypt, Howard is well-known on the conference circuit, presenting talks on the mysteries of our ancient origins. He was born in South Wales, UK, and received his education at the University of Wales, Swansea, and Oxford University. Howard has two grown up daughters, and now shares his life with his philosopher partner, Jenni. They live in the old sea fishing village of Mumbles near Swansea, South Wales.

James M. Wilkie

For over 20 years, James has sought information concerning the secrets contained in the pyramids at Giza. Through meticulous research and global travel, he continued to discover numerous sources that appeared to be pointing him in a specific direction. At length, he was able to correlate and analyze this information, leading him to the conclusions that are presented in this book. James lives in Winnipeg, Manitoba Canada, and maintains the following website: www.ambilac.com

Index

Symbols

1000 year reign 34
11, August, 1999 139
11th Signal Brigade. 158
13th Baktun 34
1st Dynasty 32
4th Dynasty 128

A

A.R.E 119, 177
A.R.E. 178
Abaco Island, Bahamas 43
Abdel, Mohammed Monayin 157
Abel v
Abimelech 42
Abraham
    32, 35, 36, 37, 38, 39, 40, 41, 44, 45, 46, 49, 53, 54, 59, 182, 184
Abram 32, 33, 35, 45, 59
Abydos 24
Acacia 82, 83, 86, 97, 100, 101
AD 27
Adam 31, 32, 45, 59, 149, 168, 184, 192, 222
Africa 21–27, 151
African Eve 22
Age of Mammals 21
Ahuzzath 42
Alcione 159
Alcor 162
Alcyone 32–35, 153, 184
Aliens 34
Alnilam 183, 184
Alnitak 26–27, 183, 184
Alpha Omega 207
Alpha star 151
Ambilac vii, 195, 196
Americans 150
Amorites 34
Angel 30, 47

Angels 205, 206
Anomalous radar rings 139, 141
Antechamber 97, 108
Anu 149
Anunnaki 146, 147, 148, 149, 150, 151, 152, 156, 157, 158, 189
Apollo 151
April 27, 2000 193
Archangel Gabriel 205
Area 51 141
Argonauts 151
Aries 26–27
Ark 58, 66, 83, 84, 85, 109, 162
Ark of the Covenant 114, 223
Armageddon 30, 192
Ascending passageway 107, 108, 111, 113, 114
Ascension 31, 34, 35, 38, 118, 189, 203
As'enath 51
Aset 27
Ashtar 148
Associated Press 195
Association for Research and Enlightenment 119, 177, 178
Assyria 151
Astarte 148
Atef crown 24
Aten 23–27
Atlantis 148, 150
Atum 23
Aurora 186
Ausar 23
Auset 27

B

Ba 26–27
Baal and Taut of Phoenicia 26–27
Babel 31
Baboon 52
Babylon 26
Badlands 157
Bahamas 43
Baktun 24, 34, 37
BBC 184
BCE 27
Beijing 21
Ben-o'ni 50

Benjamin 52, 53, 159
Bessing 155
Betel 192
Betel-HAM 29
Betelgeuse 183, 184, 224
Betelguese 192
Bethle 45
Bethlehem 29, 50
Bethlehem Processionway vi, 194, 197, 200
Bethlehem star 224
Birth Event 202
Black pyramid 79, 80
Black triangular UFO 139
Blondes 148
Blue Grid 218, 219, 220, 221
Booby trap vi
Bopp, Thomas 151
Boylan, Rick Dr. 42, 56
Brahma 159
Bright Star 158
Brookhaven 203
Brookhaven Laboratories 198
Buddha Sakia of India 26–27

C

C3 satellite 195
C3 Solar satellite 199
Caelum 147
Cain v, 32, 134
Cainan 184
Cairo 26, 51, 73, 130, 133, 143, 157, 158, 165, 182, 184, 196
Caliph, Al Ma'mun 108
Cambrian 21
Canaan 48, 51
Canis Major 151
Canis Minor 151
Capstones 162
Carboniferous 147
Cathie, Captain Bruce 136, 186
Caucasus 25–27, 26
Cayce, Edgar 119, 177, 178
CE 27
Cenzoic 21
Cetian alliance 147

Cetians 147
Cetus 147
Chaldeans 45, 137, 198, 200
Chaldeon 32
Champollin, Jean-François xix
Cheops 67, 120, 124, 128, 161
Cherubim 85, 92, 100, 102
Chichen Itza 153
Chimps 22
China 153
Circumcise 36, 38
CME v, 136, 140, 141, 183, 186, 193, 195, 201, 204
Cole 64
Comet Hale-Bopp 151
Comet Halley 151
Comet Lee
    v, 34, 129, 130, 133, 134, 135, 138, 139, 140, 142, 143, 144
Common Era 27
Continental shelf 195
Coronal Mass Ejection v, 35, 136, 183, 186, 221
Coronal Mass Ejections 140, 193, 201
Council 142, 143
Covenant 66, 67, 83, 109, 118
Crop circle 37, 56, 165, 172
Crystal
    83, 118, 129, 130, 131, 132, 133, 153, 155, 156, 158, 182, 194, 197
Crystal Global Grid 143
Crystal Grid 141
Cydonia 187

D

D and M Pyramid of Mars 185
David, Dr. Hathaway 199
December 21, 2000 v, 39, 134
December 21, 2012
    34, 37, 79, 129, 130, 133, 134, 135, 153, 155, 163, 165, 170, 188
December 21st, 2012 144
December 25th 26–27
Decimal Point 31
Delta planet 147
Descending Passageway 108, 110, 122
Devonian 21
Diamonds 147
Divine ratio 161

DNA 22, 29, 38, 51, 149, 155, 216
Doctrine of Numbers 160
Dog star 151
Dogon tribe 151
Dormion, Gilles 109
Draco 141, 143, 144
Draconians 141, 143, 147, 155
Draconis 148
Dreamland 141
Drone devices 140
Drones 140
Duat 26–27

E

Earth 165
East corner 112
Easter Island 143, 153
Edgar Morton iv
Edgar, Morton 73
Edom 41, 51
Egypt iv, vii, viii, xviii, xix, 25, 27, 31, 151, 158
Egyptian pantheon 25
Eisenhower, President 203
El-El'ohe 48
Electromagnetic 129, 130, 131, 132, 135, 136
Electromagnetic field 34
Elnil 58, 192
Elohim 149
End time 34
Enk 149
Enki 149
Enlightenment 159
Enlil 149, 150
Ennead 24–27, 25
Enoch 62, 64, 65, 223
Enosh 32, 60, 184
Ephraim 39
Ephrath 50
Ephriam 204
Ephron 53
Epsilon 147
Eridanean 189
Eridanus 189
Eridanus Delta 147

Eridean 146
Eridean Plasma Carriers 147
Erideans 146, 147, 150, 157
Esau 40, 41, 42, 47, 49, 50, 51, 156, 157, 182
Etherian 133
Etherian Guardians 133
Etherian Warriors 133
Etheric Watchers 133
Ethiopia 20, 20–27
Euphrates 29, 30, 32, 47, 147
Evadamic-Draconian 148
Eve 33, 149, 168
Exodus
    82, 83, 85, 86, 87, 88, 89, 90, 91, 92, 93, 94, 95, 96, 97, 98, 99, 100, 101, 102, 116, 162, 165, 222

F

Face, The 185, 187
Falcon 27
Falcon god 25–27
Fatima 202
Fifth, The Element 205
Final Countdown 146, 155
First Time 222
First Wave 135
Flash 144
Flash radar 206
Foreskin 36, 38
Fountain of Youth 217
Fourth generation 34
Frankincense 38, 39
Free will 133, 138, 149, 150
Freemasonry 151

G

Galactic Council 142
Galactic Federation 148, 152
Garden of Eden 31, 32, 59, 222
Gatenbrink, Rudolph 65, 75, 117, 118
Gaza Plateau 223
Geb 23
Genesis
    v, 20, 29, 31, 32, 34, 35, 38, 39, 40, 44, 59, 82, 129, 131, 132, 134, 153, 162, 165, 192, 222
Genetic code 31
Geology 195

Geomagnetic activity 186
Gerar 42
Giza 221
Giza complex 174
Giza Plateau 20, 26–
    27, 27, 28, 30, 31, 44, 46, 49, 50, 51, 53, 138, 143, 153, 154, 155, 161, 163, 174–
    180, 184, 190, 194, 196, 222
Global Grid 143, 185, 190
Global warming 43
Glyphs 174, 197
Godwara 21
Gold 38, 82, 83, 84, 85, 86, 87, 91, 92, 94, 99, 100, 101
Golden calf 23
Gomorrah 150
Gorillas 22
Grand Alignment 183, 184
Grand Gallery
    65, 66, 76, 80, 81, 82, 83, 86, 87, 90, 91, 92, 94, 95, 101, 102, 105, 109, 115, 122, 182, 223
Granite Plugs 108
Great Ennead of Heliopolis 25–27
Great Experiment 190, 225
Great Gallery 105
Great Pyramid
    75, 83, 109, 112, 114, 116, 117, 120, 160, 162, 163, 200, 221
Great pyramid 108
Great Step 96, 104, 115, 123
Green Stone Trail (New Zealand) 143
Greys 145, 148, 203
Grid 188, 191, 192, 194, 196, 197, 198, 201, 202
Grid, Blue 191
Grid, Red 191, 204
Grotto 105
Guardians 133, 137, 194

H

HAARP 130, 136, 139
Hagar 35
Hale, Alan 151
Hale Bopp 148
Hall of Records 39, 40, 51, 123, 125, 127, 164, 173, 176
Halo event 186
Ham 184
Haran 32, 33, 44, 45
Harmony of the Spheres 160

Harp star 151
Hawass, Zahi 119
Hebron 40
Heliopolis 23–27, 25
Helix 163, 171
Herme 151
Hermopolis 52, 159
Heru 27
Hidden Room 92, 95, 161
Hieratic script 200
Hieroglyphic 200
Hieroglyphs 174–180
High Council 38
High Frequency Active Auroral Research Program 130, 136
Himalayan 21
Hittite 53
Hittites 40, 53
Homo sapiens 20–21, 149, 222
Hope, Murray 151
HOR 67, 74
Horus 23, 25, 31, 32, 58, 124, 125, 128, 173, 177, 182, 222
Hubble Space Telescope 151
Humanoid 29
Humanoids 148

I

Ibis 52, 159
Indra of Tibet 26–27
Interdimensional Physics 195
Ionospheric research instrument 136
Iraq 25–27
IRI 136
Iron Pins 88
Isaac 37, 40, 41, 42, 44, 45, 46, 47, 49, 50, 53, 54
Iscah 33
Ishmael 35, 37, 38
Isis 23, 24–27, 30, 31, 33, 37, 56, 173, 202, 222
Isis-Alnitac 71
Israel 29, 30, 47, 48, 49, 50, 52, 53, 54, 59
Itinerants 28
Iunu 51

J

Jabbok 47

Jacob
    28, 29, 30, 40, 41, 42, 44, 46, 47, 48, 49, 50, 51, 52, 53, 54, 59, 156, 157, 224
Jacob's ladder 30, 42
Jao of Nepal 26–27
Japeth 192
JAPETH-JARED 29
Jared 32–35, 61, 184
Jeff Rense Sightings vi
Jehovah 149
Jesus 25, 27, 217
Johanson 20–27
Joseph
    28, 41, 45, 46, 50, 51, 52, 53, 54, 55, 58, 59, 182, 192, 197, 202
Joseph, Dr. Schor 119
Jupiter 142, 147, 151, 157, 183, 184, 188, 199, 202, 224
Jurassic 21
Jurassic Park 148

K

Kaphre 173, 176
Keeper of the Key 23
Kenan 184
Kenya 20
Key 77
Khafre 50, 124, 126, 127, 128, 161, 228
Khafre's Mortuary Temple 126
Khafre's Valley Temple 71, 72
Khaphre 175
Khefre 173
Khem 26
Khepera 23, 26
Khrishna of Hundostan 26–27
Khufu
    64, 66, 67, 68, 70, 71, 112, 120, 124, 126, 127, 128, 160, 161, 172, 175, 192, 223
Khufu's mortuary temple 125
King, Julie 221
King's Chamber 116, 123, 176, 223

L

Laban 45, 46
Lamp stand 101
Lamp-Stand 89
Lampstands 90
LASCO 140, 144, 188, 193, 201

Laurussia 21–27
Lazar, Robert 73
Leah 45
Leakey 20–27
Ledges 80, 83, 84, 86, 91, 97, 98, 100, 103, 104, 106, 107
Lee, Steven 34
Light Workers 201
Lockheed-Martin 206
Long Count calendar 144
Lord to the Limit 23
Los Alamos, New Mexico 199
Lot 33
Love Bug" virus 196
Lower (Northern) Egypt 32
Lower Egypt 25–27, 32
Lucy 20
Luz 45
Lyra 148
Lyran 148
Lyre 151

M

M class flares 183
M45 199
Machpelah 39, 40, 53
Machu Pichu 153
Mahalaleel 32, 184
Mahalele 61
Majestic Twelve Operation 203
Major, John Jenkins 144
Mali 151
Mamre 40, 53
Mars 34, 38, 47, 51, 59, 150, 152, 157, 161, 165, 173, 183, 184
Mars Global Surveyor 187
Marshall Space Flight Center 199
Mary 202
Maser 162
Masters, Marshall 135
Matrix, The 206
Matter 131, 132
May 12, 2000 207, 221
May 13, 2000 202
May 3, 2000 v
May 5, 2000 182

May 5, 2000 175, 184, 190, 192, 196
Mayan 21, 142, 144, 165, 174
Mediterranean 147
Menkaura 127
Menkaure 67, 71, 124, 125, 126, 127, 128, 175
Mercator 186
Mercury 33, 41, 45, 165, 183, 199
Mesopotamia 25–27, 132, 137
Methuselah 62, 64, 65, 223
Mexico 143, 153
MGS 187
Michel, Aime 185
Middle Pleistocene 21
Milcah 33
Mind controllers 189
Mintaka 183
Mintake 184
Mitochondrial DNA 22
MJ-12 43, 203
MJ-12 Group 203
Molecular clock 22
Monolith 42, 43
Montauk research   project 145
Moody, Wayne 217
Moon 23, 43, 44
Moroney 27
Mortuary Temple 126
Mubarak, Hosni 157
Muslim 108
Myrrh 38

N

Nahor 32, 33, 45
NASA 136, 183, 186, 193, 206
National Aeronautical Space Agency 140
National Geographic Organization 177
National Security Council 43, 203
Navy SEAL 43
Neb-er-djer 23
Nefilim 149
Nellis Naval 141
Nephthys 23
Neters 27
New Grange (Ireland) 143

New Mexico 199
New Millennium news 195
Nibiru 149
Nile 24, 26, 33, 147
Nile Valley 27
Nine gods of the Ennead 25
Noah 64, 150, 184, 192, 223
Noah's Ark 83, 135, 162
Nohor 45
Nordic 32, 148
Nordics 148
Nostradamus 34, 129, 135, 191
November 17, 1999 139
Now 23
NSA 40, 42, 131
NSC 42, 203
Nu 23
Nuit 23
Nun 22, 30, 222
Nut 23
Nut, Sky Goddess 23

O

O., Peter Erbe 159
Odin 26–27
Ogdoad 159
Ogdoad of Hermopolis 52
Old Kingdom 128
Olduvai Gorge 20
ON 26, 28, 36, 51, 56
Orang-utans 22
ORCA 140
Orion 26, 27, 59, 148, 183, 184, 192, 222
Orion Empire 148
Orions 29, 143, 224
Orion's belt 183
Orpheus 151
Osiris 23, 24, 25, 26, 27, 30, 31, 33, 40, 56, 58, 176, 192, 222

P

Paleontologists 224
Pangaea 21–27
Parallel Universes 216
Patrice, Jean Godin 109

PEA 194
Pentagon 196
Penuel 48
Peru 153
Pharaoh Khufu 76
Phi 160, 161, 165, 168, 169
Phicol 42
Philadelphia Experiment 142, 145
Philadelphia Naval Yard 145
Phoenix Projects 142
photon 158, 159
Photon Belt 153
photon belt 159
Physical Evidence Acquisition 194
Pi 160, 161, 165, 168, 169, 170
Piazzi Smyth 64
Pic du Midi Observatory 151
Plasma Beam Carrier 143
Plasma Carrier 140, 141, 157, 188, 201
Plasma Carriers v, 146, 147
Plasma Discharge Theory 136
Plasma Target Specific Bombers 140
Pleiades 29, 32, 38, 148, 153, 159, 162, 184, 199, 201
Pleiadian 29, 45, 47
Pleiadians 29, 141, 145, 154, 224
Plejarians 141, 142
Pluto 157
Pope 202
Portcullis 97, 108, 123
Portugal 202
Poti'phera 51
Pringle, Lucy 165
Processionway 67, 71, 125
Procyo 151
Procyon 148, 151
Project Rainbow 145
Promethus of the Caucasus 26–27
Prophecy, The 205
Proton Flux 191
Purple Grid 204
Pyramid complex 20
Pyramid of Khufu 125
Pyrenees 21
Pythagoras 160

Q

Queen's Chamber
    86, 89, 93, 95, 96, 104, 109, 110, 111, 113, 114, 115, 116, 117, 175, 223
Queen's Pyramid 76, 182

R

Ra 22, 23, 24, 25, 26, 222
Ra-Harakhte 23
Rachel 45
Radar ring activity 196, 198
Radar rings 130
Re 23, 30, 52, 152, 153, 154
Re-atum 51
Re-Harakhty 51
Rebekah 53
Receiver pyramid 180
Red granite 108
Red grid 196, 204, 219, 220
Refraction 145
Remote Viewing 29, 133, 137
Remote viewing 150
Rense, Jeff vi, 194, 197
Reptilian 29, 32, 36, 40, 45, 47, 51, 118, 145, 224
Reptilian hybrid 148
Reptiloids 148
Reptoid 146, 147
Reptoid Klingons 146
Research and Development Intelligence Operation 203
Resurrection myths 25–27
Revelation 165, 172, 201
Richard, Dr. Boylan 56
Rigel 151
RNA 51
Rodina 21
Rosetta stone xix
Rosicrucians 151
Rostau 26–27
Roswell, New Mexico 203
Rudolph Gatenbrink 65, 75
Russians 150
Rusty 144
RV 137

S

Sacred Geometry 216
Sacred sites 139, 143
Sanctuary 82, 101, 109
Saqqara 26–27
Sarah 37, 39, 40, 53
Sarai 37
Sarcophagus 75, 119, 121, 176, 197
Sarich, Vince 22
Sasquatch 148
Satellite pyramid 50
Saturn 183, 184, 199, 224
Scarab beetle 23
Schele, Linda 144
Schor Foundation New York 119
Schor, Joseph 119
SEC 198
Second Veil 122
Second Wave 191
Secret Service 43
Seir 51
Se'ir 51
Sender 179
Sender pyramid 180
September 21, 1999 134
September 22, 1999 140
Set 25
Seth 27, 31, 32, 33, 59, 184, 223
SETH-SHEM 29
SG 1 145
Shades of Mirror Imaging 78
Shafts 64, 65, 105, 117, 119, 177, 178
Shamballa 217
Shan 148
Shechem 49
Shem 184, 192
Showbread 89
Shu 23, 24–27
Silurian 21
Sima de los Huesos 21
Sinai 158
Sirian 143
Sirians 148, 224
Sirius 59, 148, 151, 222

Sirius B 151
Sirius-B 148
Sister Lucia 202
Skull and Crossbones 177
Slave masters 189
Smyth, Piazzi 64
Sodom 150
SOHO 140, 188, 193, 195, 198
SOL 148
Sol System 148
Solar Cruiser 201
Solar Cycle 183
Solar eclipse 27, 129, 134, 139, 144
Solar flare activity 139
Solar flares 186
Solar Max 199
Solar torpedo 193
South American 147
South Gallery wall 113
South wall 114, 121
Space Environment Center 198
Spain 21
Sphinx 67, 69, 72, 74, 119, 161
Spiritists 151
Standiford USAF 141
Star Alignment 178
Star Children 216
Star of Bethlehem 192
Star X 192
Star Y 192
Stargate 140, 142, 145, 178, 181, 183, 185, 190, 198, 224
Startrek 146
Stonehenge 143, 153
Subterranean Chamber 76, 81, 114, 120, 121, 122, 123, 124, 126
Sulawesi 195
Sun v, xiv, 23–27, 199
Sun Cruiser 140, 157, 188
Sunspot 186
Syria 26
Syrian 29, 38

T

Tammuz of Syria and Babylon 26–27
Targeting 139

Tau Cetians 147
Taurus 141, 147
Taut of Phoenicia 26–27
Tefnut 23
Tem 23, 26
Temple of Isis 77
Terah 32
Terra 28, 148, 152, 188–190, 192
Tetrahedron 162
Third Wave 192
Thoth 23, 30, 52, 154, 222
Three lineages 29
Three Tombs 120
Three Waves 191
Three wise men 38
Thura limestone v
Tigris 29, 32, 132, 137, 147
Time and space 34
Time of the gods 30
Time Travel 145
Time-space 145
Tomb of Osiris 118, 119, 177
Tomb of Unas 26–27
Tompkins, Peter 67
Tower of Babel 56
Transmigration of Souls 160
Transmitter 179
Transmitter pyramid 180
Travelers 204
Trebor, Robert 151
Tree of Knowledge 149
Tsunami 195
Turkana Basin 20
Turkey 130, 136
Twelve houses 133

U

UFO 139, 185, 203
UN Security Council 43
Unas 26–27
Unholy Six 148
United States 195, 203
Universal Grid 218, 219, 220
Universal Time 135

University of California 22
Upper Egypt 24, 25–27, 32
Upuaut 117
Upuaut Project 75
US Marines 21
Uxmal Pyramid 153

V

Valley Temple 78, 80, 125
Variable star 147
Vatican 202
Vega 148, 151
Veil 98, 99, 100, 101, 102, 105
Venus 41, 45, 59, 165, 183, 199, 202
Viking Remote Viewing 150
Virgin 22
Virishna 25–27
Vortex 178

W

Walken, Christopher 205
Weighing of the heart and feather 23
White crown 24
White Pyramids 153
Wilson, Allan 22
Wilson, Cann and Stoneking 22
Windows 204
Winged Disc 148, 151
Winged globe 151
Winged sun disc 151
Winged sun disk 23
Winged-solar-disk 151
Wolf, Dr. 42, 43, 57
World Data Center 136
World War II 145

X

X Star 165

Y

Y Star 165
Yugas 159

Z

Zaph'enath-pane'ah 51
Zep Tepi 23, 30, 31, 222
Zero degrees 32, 34
Zeta-Reticuli 203
Zetas 203
Zhoukoudian 21
Zodiac 162
Zoroaster 26